Zaner-Bloser
Handwriting

Author
Clinton S. Hackney, Ed.D.

Reviewers

Julie Althide, Teacher, Hazelwood School District, St. Louis, Missouri

Becky Brashears, Teacher, Gocio Elementary, Sarasota, Florida

Douglas Dewey, Teacher, National Heritage Academies, Grand Rapids, Michigan

Jennifer B. Dutcher, Teacher, Elk Grove School District, Sacramento, California

Gita Farbman, Teacher, School District of Philadelphia, Philadelphia, Pennsylvania

Susan Ford, Teacher, St. Ann's School, Charlotte, North Carolina

Brenda Forehand, Teacher, David Lipscomb Middle School, Nashville, Tennessee

Sharon Hall, Teacher, USD 443, Dodge City, Kansas

Sr. James Madeline, Teacher, St. Anthony School, Allston, Massachusetts

Lori A. Martin, Teacher, Chicago Public Schools, Chicago, Illinois

Vikki F. McCurdy, Teacher, Mustang School District, Oklahoma City, Oklahoma

Melissa Neary Morgan, Reading Specialist, Fairfax County Public Schools, Fairfax, Virginia

Sue Postlewait, Literacy Resource Consultant, Marshall County Schools, Moundsville, West Virginia

Gloria C. Rivera, Principal, Edinburg CISO, Edinburg, Texas

Rebecca Rollefson, Teacher, Ericsson Community School, Minneapolis, Minnesota

Susan Samsa, Teacher, Dover City Schools, Dover, Ohio

Zelda J. Smith, Instructional Specialist, New Orleans Public Schools, New Orleans, Louisiana

Early Childhood Consultant: Jo Beecher Prather, Reading and Early Childhood Specialist, Madison County School District, Madison, MS

Occupational Therapy Consultant: Maureen E. King, O.T.R.

Credits

Art: Mariano Gil: 3, 4, 6, 8, 9, 37, 38, 39, 40, 41, 42, 43, 45, 46, 47, 48, 49, 50, 51, 53, 54, 55, 56, 57, 58, 59, 61, 62, 63, 64, 65, 66, 67, 69, 70, 71, 72, 73, 74, 75, 76, 77, 79, 80, 81, 82, 83, 84, 85, 86, 87, 89, 90, 91, 92, 93, 94, 95, 97, 98, 99, 100, 101, 102, 103, 118, 119; Susan Lexa: 4, 112, 113, 114, 115, 116, 117; Sharron O'Neil: 3, 16, 17, 20, 21, 24, 25, 28, 29, 32, 33, 35, 36, 105, 106, 107, 108, 109, 110, 111; Andy San Diego: 10, 11

Photos: George C. Anderson Photography, Inc.: 12–13

Development: Kirchoff/Wohlberg, Inc., in collaboration with Zaner-Bloser Educational Publishers

ISBN-13 978-0-7367-5142-1

ISBN-10 0-7367-5142-4

10 11 13880 6

Zaner-Bloser, Inc., P.O. Box 16764, Columbus, Ohio 43216-6764

1-800-421-3018

www.zaner-bloser.com

Printed in the United States of America

Contents

Unit 1: Getting Started

Unit 2: Learning Basic Strokes

Unit 3: Writing Letters

Unit 4: Writing Numerals

Unit 5: Using What You Have Learned

FISH	ELEPHANT	DUCK	CAMEL	BEAR	ANT
LION	KITE	JAM	INSECTS	HEN	GUITAR
RAINBOW	QUEEN	PIG	OCTOPUS	NEST	MOON
FOX	WAGON	VASE	UMBRELLA	TRAIN	SUN
				ZEBRA	YO-YO

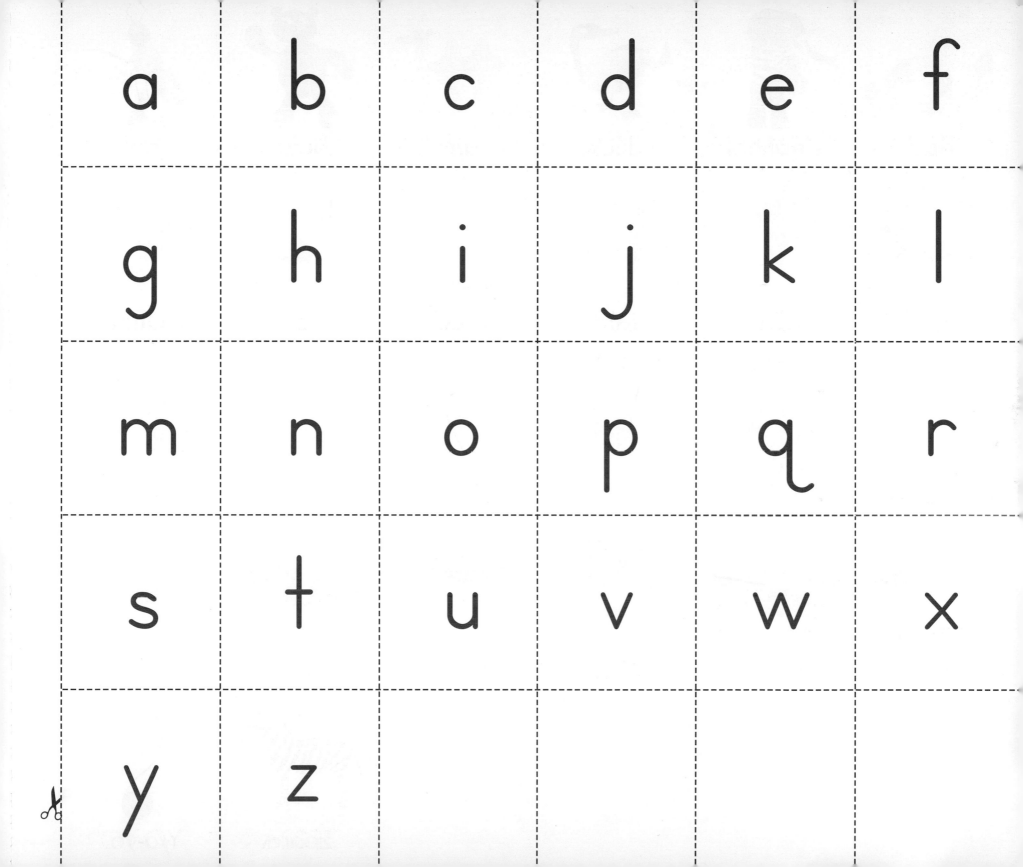

fish	elephant	duck	camel	bear	ant
lion	kite	jam	insects	hen	guitar
rainbow	queen	pig	octopus	nest	moon
fox	wagon	vase	umbrella	train	sun
				zebra	yo-yo

Show What You Can Do

Draw a picture.

Write letters you know.

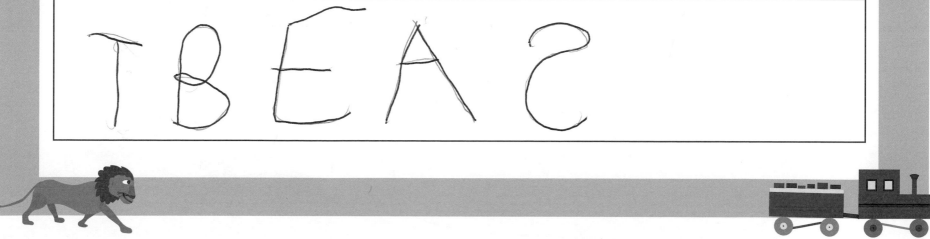

You use your hands when you write.

Draw your **left** hand on this mitten.

Many children use their left hand to write.

Draw your **right** hand on this mitten.

Which hand do you use to hold your pencil?

Writing Positions

If you write with your  left hand. . .

Sit up tall.

Keep your feet on the floor.

Slant your paper.

Put both arms on the desk.

Pull your pencil toward your left elbow.

Use your right hand to move the paper.

Hold the pencil like this.

Do not squeeze the pencil when you write.

If you write with your  right hand. . .

Sit up tall.
Keep both feet on the floor.

Keep your paper straight.

Put both arms on the desk.

Pull your pencil toward the middle of your body.

Use your left hand to move the paper.

Hold the pencil like this.

Do not squeeze the pencil when you write.

13

Your Book

Look for these in your handwriting book.

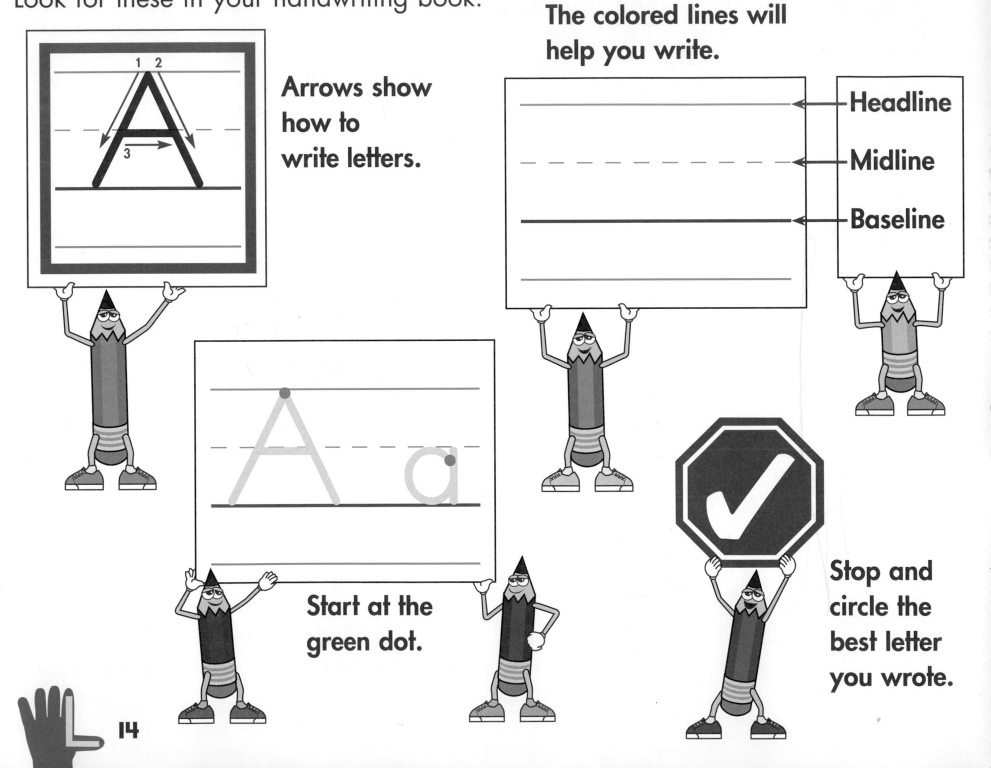

Arrows show how to write letters.

The colored lines will help you write.

Headline

Midline

Baseline

Start at the green dot.

Stop and circle the best letter you wrote.

Vertical Lines

You use vertical lines when you write.
Place your vertical strokes here.
Trace them with your finger.

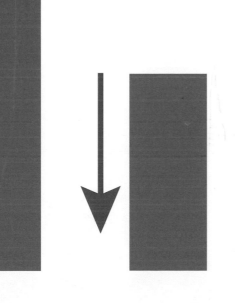

Find vertical lines in the picture.
Draw this picture or one of your own.

Write vertical lines.
Start at the ●. Stop at the ●.

Basic Strokes Vertical Lines

Write vertical lines.

Start at the ●. Stop at the ●.

Trace the lines.

Use your finger to trace the vertical lines
in letters and numerals.

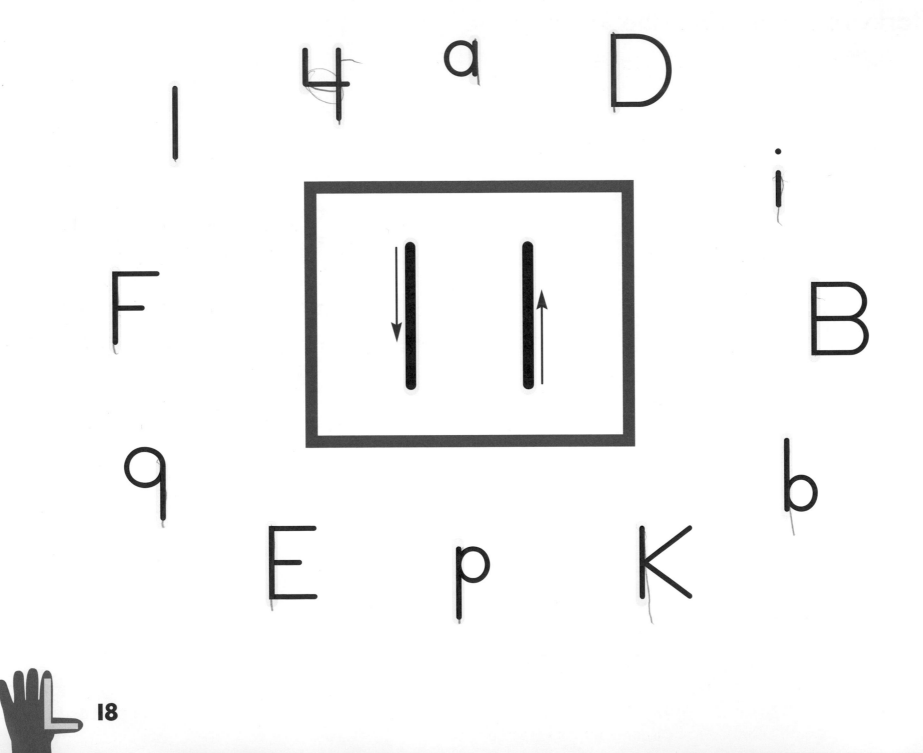

Basic Strokes Horizontal Lines

You use horizontal lines when you write.
Place your horizontal strokes here.
Trace them with your finger.

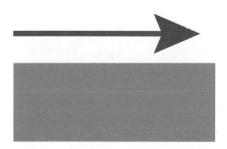

Find horizontal lines in the picture.
Draw this picture or one of your own.

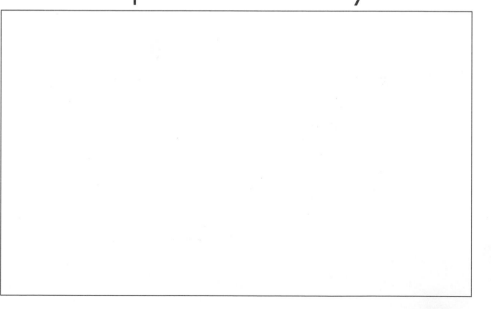

Write horizontal lines.
Start at the ●. Stop at the ●.

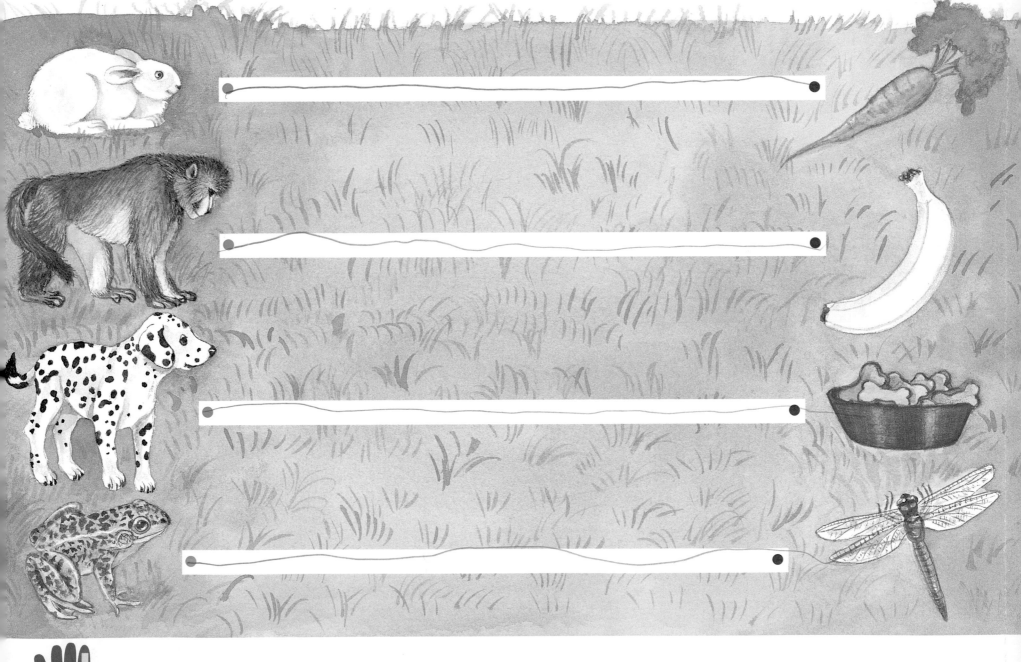

Basic Strokes **Horizontal Lines**

Write horizontal lines.
Start at the ●. Stop at the ●.

Trace the lines.

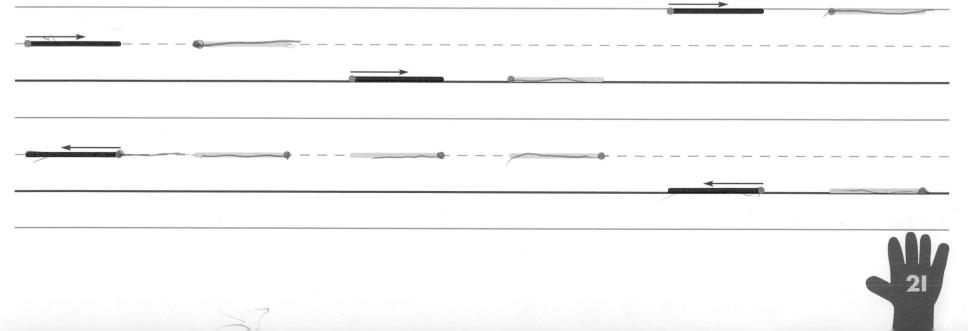

Use your finger to trace the horizontal lines in letters and numerals.

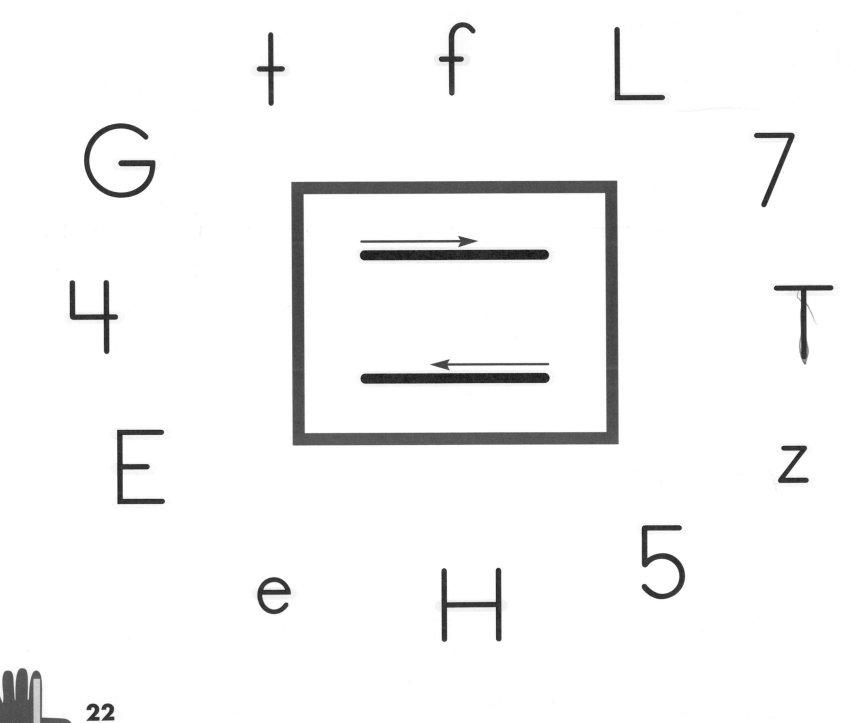

Backward Circle Lines

You use backward circle lines when you write.
Place your circle strokes here.
Trace them with your finger.

Find circle lines in the picture.
Draw this picture or one of
your own.

Write backward circle lines.
Start at the ●. Stop at the ●.

24

Backward Circle Lines

Write backward circle lines.
Start at the ●. Stop at the ●.

Trace the lines.

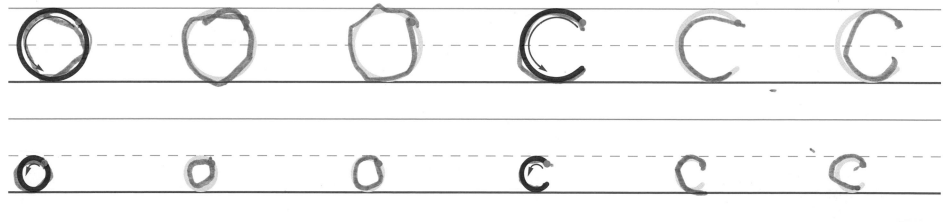

25

Use your finger to trace the backward circle lines in letters and numerals.

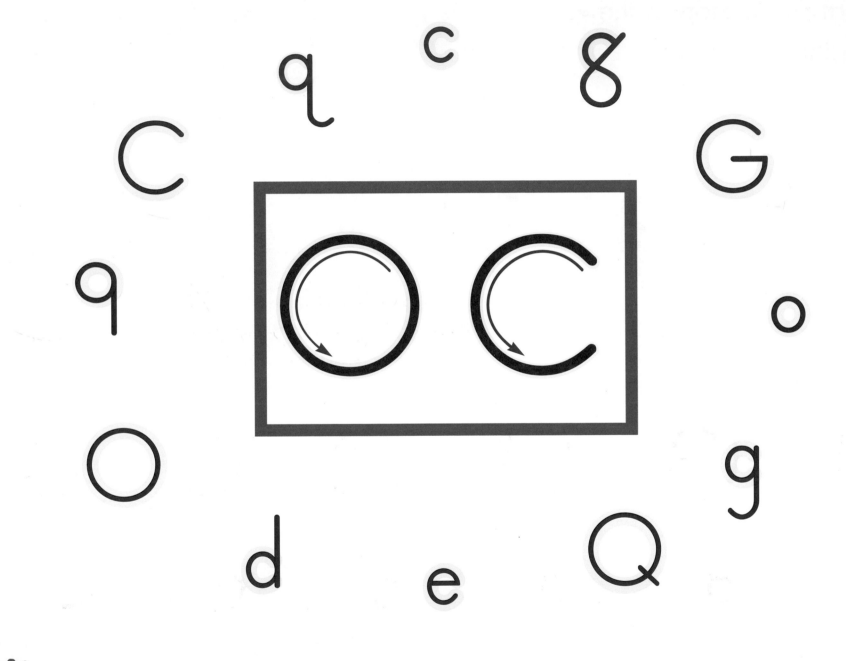

You use slant lines when you write.
Place your slant strokes here.
Trace them with your finger.

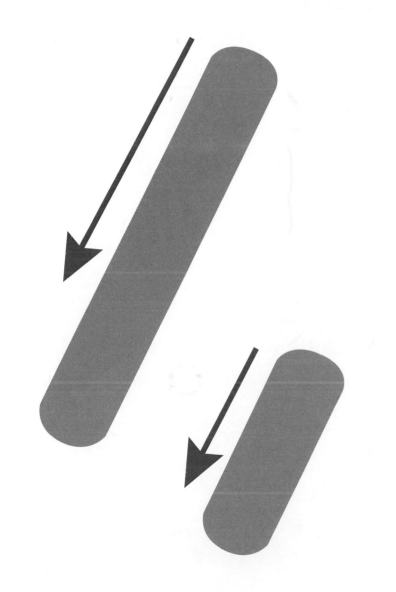

Find slant lines in the picture.
Draw this picture or one of your own.

27

Write slant lines.
Start at the ●. Stop at the ●.

Basic Strokes Slant Lines

Write slant lines.

Start at the . Stop at the ●.

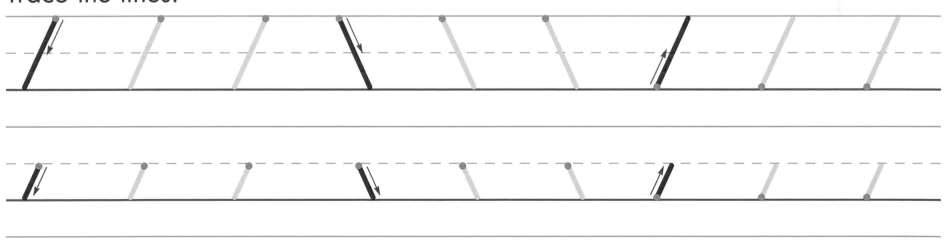

Trace the lines.

29

Use your finger to trace the slant lines
in letters and numerals.

z   k   w

A   7

N   X

2   Y

x   W   v

You use forward circle lines when you write.

Place your circle strokes here.

Trace them with your finger.

Find circle lines in the picture.

Draw this picture or one of

your own.

Write forward circle lines.
Start at the ●. Stop at the ●.

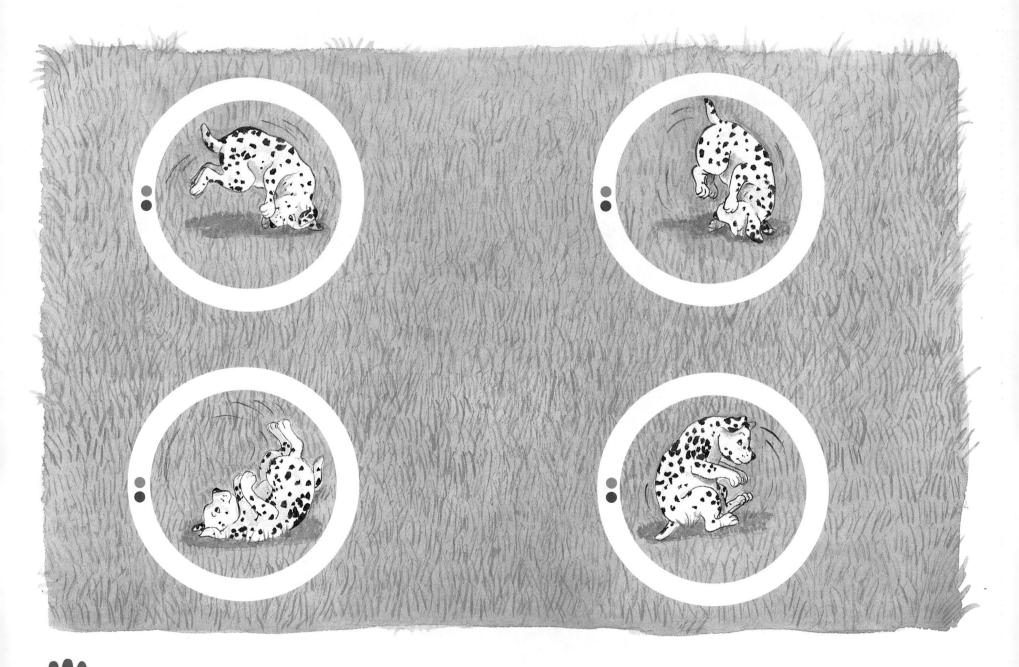

32

Forward Circle Lines

Write forward circle lines.
Start at the ●. Stop at the ●.

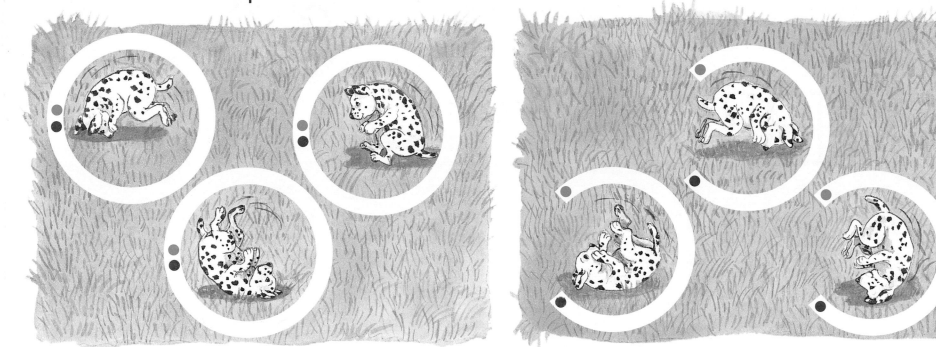

Trace the lines.

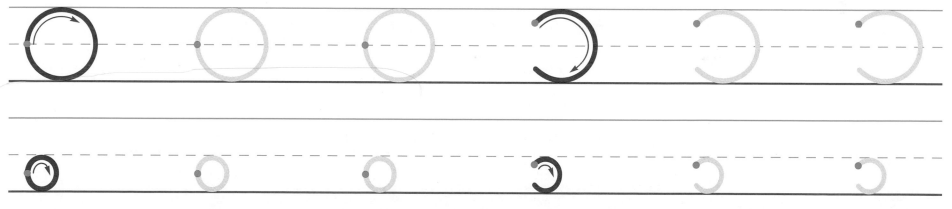

Use your finger to trace the forward circle lines
in letters and numerals.

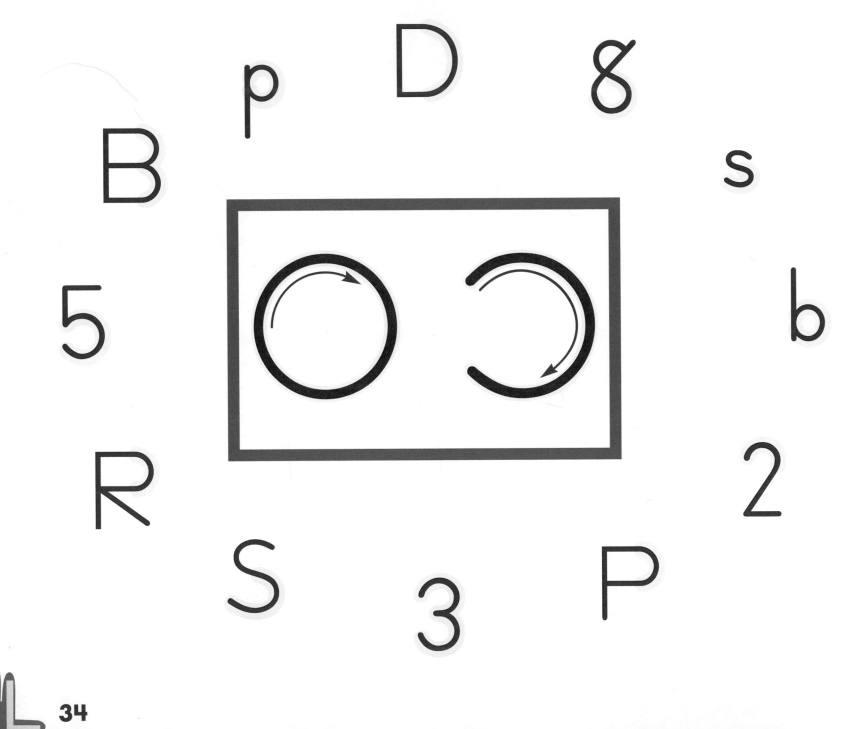

Four Kinds of Lines

Use basic strokes to draw the picture frames.

Use basic strokes to draw a line around each kite.

A B C D E F G H I J K **L** M N O P Q R S T U V W X Y Z
a b c d e f g h i j k **l** m n o p q r s t u v w x y z

Lemonade

Trace and write.

L L L L L

L L L L

Lemonade Len Lisa

Stroke description to guide letter formation at home:

Pull down straight.
Slide right.

Directions: Discuss the picture on the page.
Help children identify **L** in the word on the sign.

37

School to Home

A B C D E F G H I J K L M N O P Q R S T U V W X Y Z
a b c d e f g h i j k l m n o p q r s t u v w x y z

L
l

lion

leaf

lemon

Trace and write.

lion   leaf   lemon

School to Home

Stroke description to guide letter formation at home:

Pull down straight.

Directions: Discuss the picture on the page. Help children identify **l** in the words that name the pictures.

I i

Insect Island

Trace and write.

Insect Island   Ike

Stroke description to guide letter formation at home:

Pull down straight. Lift.
Slide right. Lift. Slide right.

Directions: Discuss the picture on the page.
Help children identify **I** in the words on the sign.

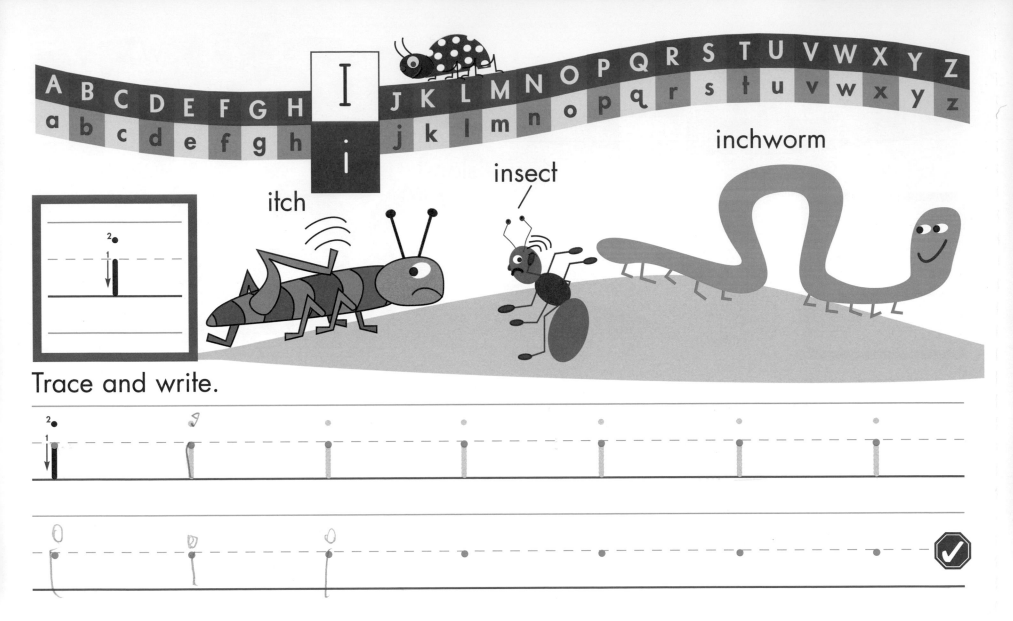

A B C D E F G H **I** J K L M N O P Q R S T U V W X Y Z
a b c d e f g h **i** j k l m n o p q r s t u v w x y z

itch

insect

inchworm

Trace and write.

inchworm   itch   insect

School to Home

Stroke description to guide letter formation at home:

Pull down straight. Lift. Dot.

Directions: Discuss the picture on the page. Help children identify **i** in the words that name the pictures.

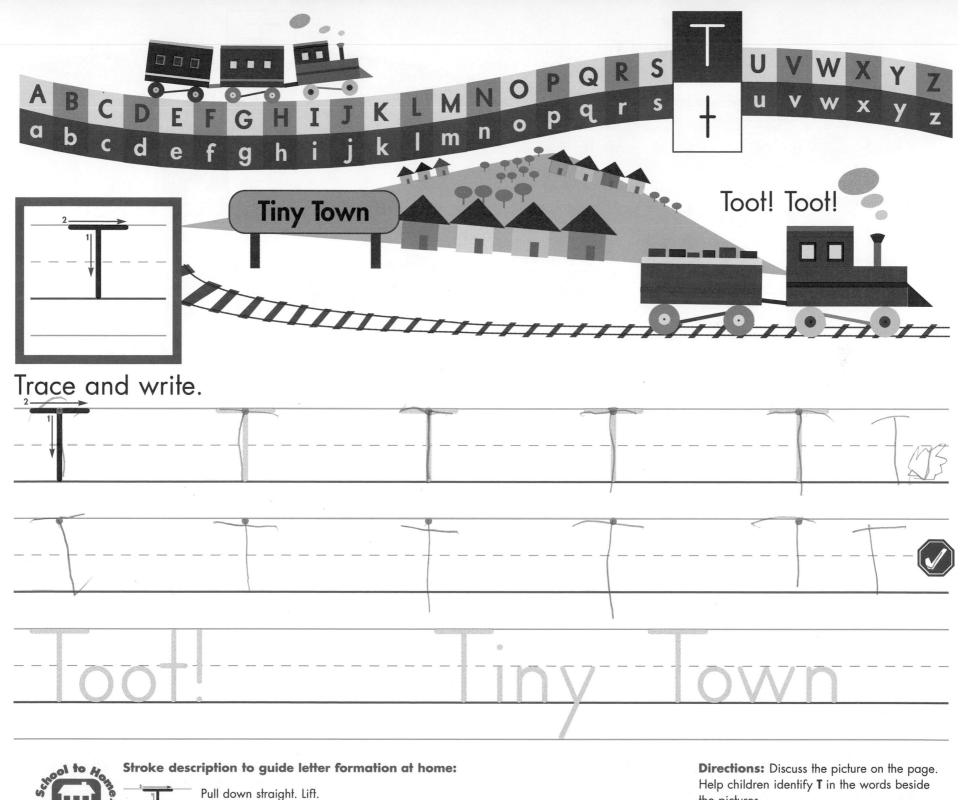

A B C D E F G H I J K L M N O P Q R S T U V W X Y Z
a b c d e f g h i j k l m n o p q r s t u v w x y z

T
t

Tiny Town

Toot! Toot!

Trace and write.

Toot!   Tiny Town

Stroke description to guide letter formation at home:

Pull down straight. Lift.
Slide right.

Directions: Discuss the picture on the page. Help children identify **T** in the words beside the pictures.

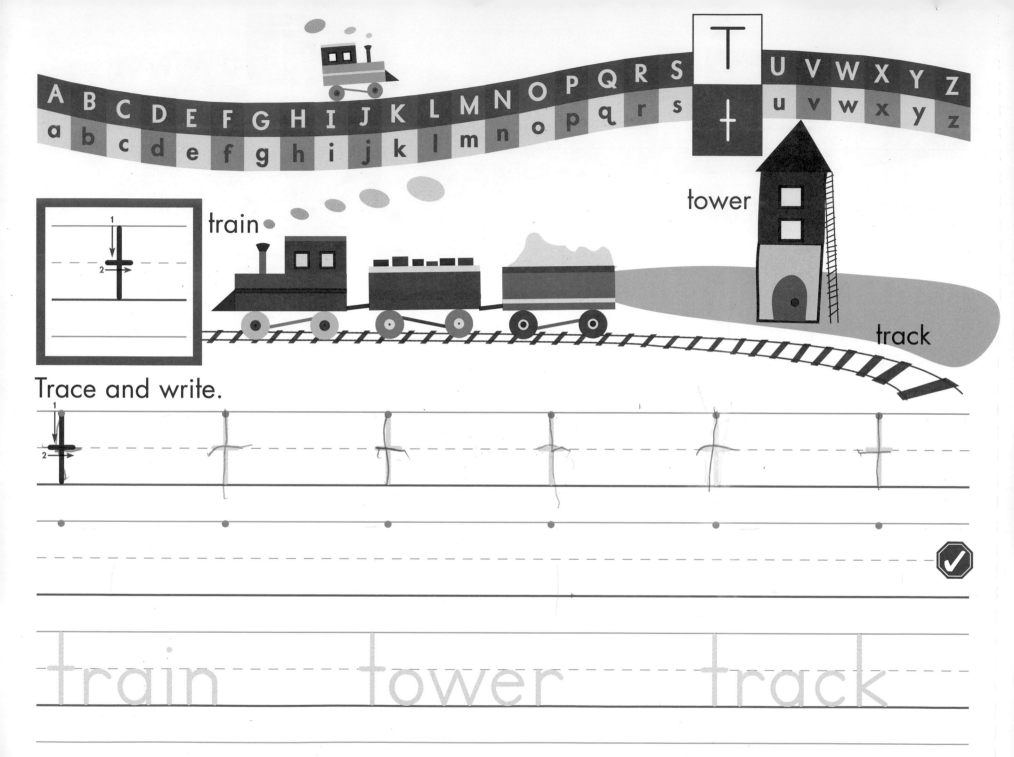

train

tower

track

Trace and write.

train   tower   track

School to Home

Stroke description to guide letter formation at home:

Pull down straight. Lift. Slide right.

Directions: Discuss the picture on the page. Help children identify **t** in the words that name the pictures.

Practice

Write the letters.

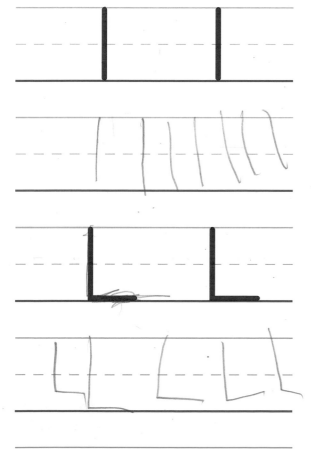
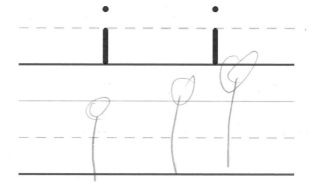
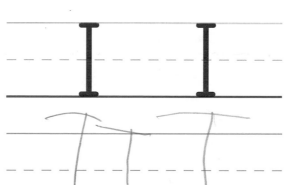
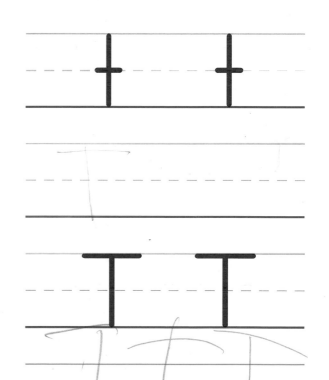

Write the Alphabet

Write the missing uppercase letters.

A B C D E

F G H J

K M N O

P Q R S

U V W X Y Z

O
O

Trace and write.

On   Off   Otto

Directions: Discuss the picture on the page. Help children identify **O** in the words on the television.

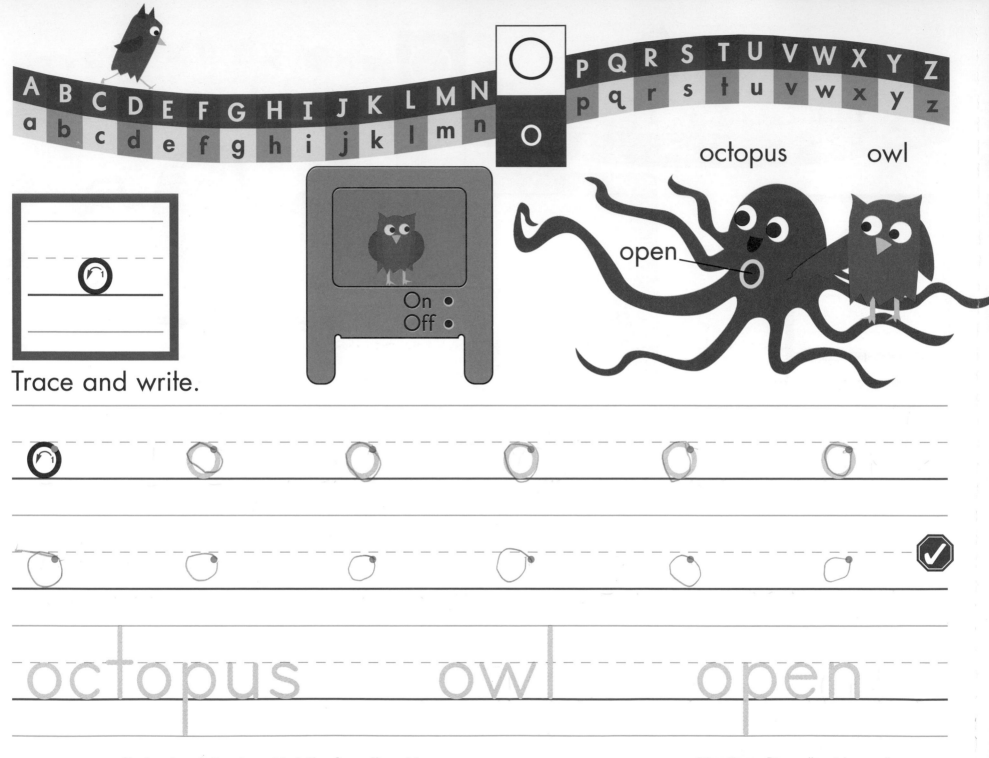

A B C D E F G H I J K L M N O P Q R S T U V W X Y Z

a b c d e f g h i j k l m n o p q r s t u v w x y z

octopus   owl

open

Trace and write.

octopus   owl   open

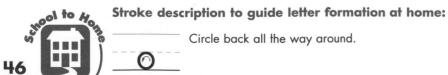

Stroke description to guide letter formation at home:

Circle back all the way around.

Directions: Discuss the picture on the page. Help children identify **o** in the words that name the pictures.

A
a

B C D E F G H I J K L M N O P Q R S T U V W X Y Z
b c d e f g h i j k l m n o p q r s t u v w x y z

AVENUE A

Trace and write.

A A A A A A

Avenue Alex Ann

School to Home

Stroke description to guide letter formation at home:

Slant left. Lift. Slant right. Lift. Slide right.

Directions: Discuss the picture on the page. Help children identify **A** in the words on the sign.

A a

B C D E F G H I J K L M N O P Q R S T U V W X Y Z
b c d e f g h i j k l m n o p q r s t u v w x y z

ants

apple

alligator

Trace and write.

a

a a a a a a a a a a a

a a a d a a a a a a ✔

apple a ants a alligator

Stroke description to guide letter formation at home:

a

Circle back all the way around;
push up straight. Pull down straight.

Directions: Discuss the picture on the page.
Help children identify **a** in the words that name
the pictures.

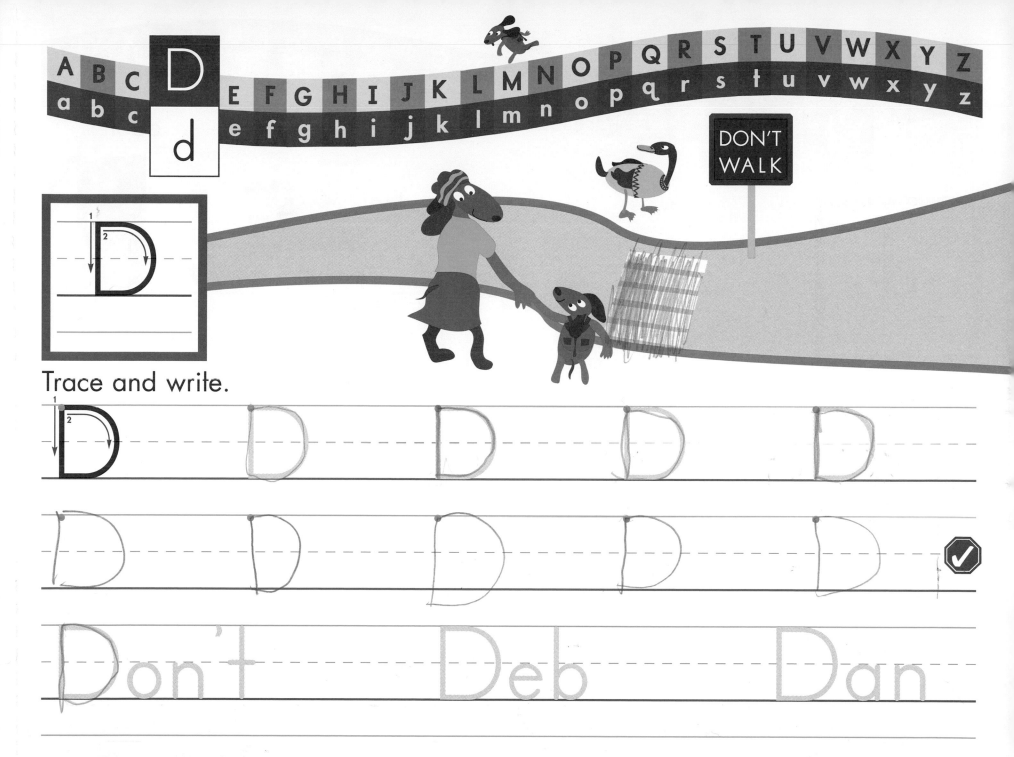

DON'T WALK

Trace and write.

D D D D D

D D D D D ✓

Don't Deb Dan

Stroke description to guide letter formation at home:

Pull down straight. Lift. Slide right; curve forward; slide left.

Directions: Discuss the picture on the page. Help children identify **D** in the words on the sign.

49

door

dog

duck

Trace and write.

d d d d d d d d

d

dog duck door

School to Home

Stroke description to guide letter formation at home:

d Circle back all the way around; push up straight. Pull down straight.

Directions: Discuss the picture on the page. Help children identify **d** in the words that name the pictures.

Practice

Write the letters.

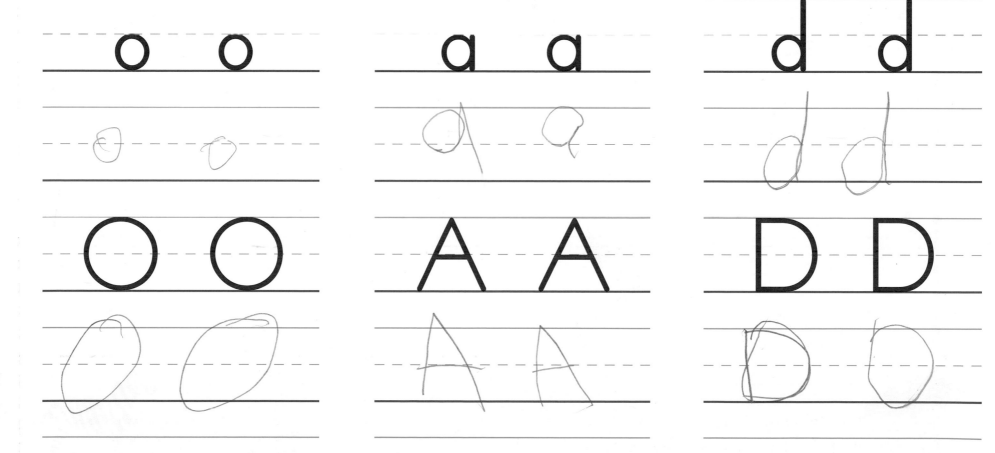

Write the Alphabet

Write the missing lowercase letters.

b   c   e

f   g   h   j

k   m   n

p   q   r   s

u   v   w   x   y   z

A B C D E F G H I J K L M N O P Q R S T U V W X Y Z
a b c d e f g h i j k l m n o p q r s t u v w x y z

Camel's Cakes

Trace and write.

C C C C C C

C C C C C C ✓

Cakes Clem Cara

Stroke description to guide letter formation at home:

C Circle back.

Directions: Discuss the picture on the page. Help children identify **C** in the words on the sign.

School to Home

53

A B C D E F G H I J K L M N O P Q R S T U V W X Y Z
a b c d e f g h i j k l m n o p q r s t u v w x y z

C
C

camel

cup

cook

Trace and write.

C c c c c c c c c c c c ✔

camel cook cup

Stroke description to guide letter formation at home:

Circle back.

C

Directions: Discuss the picture on the page. Help children identify **c** in the words that name the pictures.

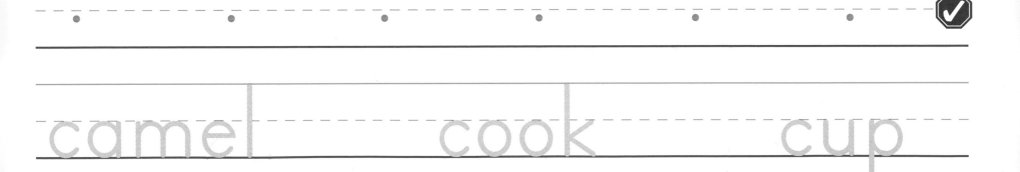

A B C D E F G H I J K L M N O P Q R S T U V W X Y Z
a b c d e f g h i j k l m n o p q r s t u v w x y z

E
e

EYE DOCTOR

E
T U
E M U
T P S O
O C T L F
V N H S E B

Trace and write.

E E E E E E

Eye Eric Elsa

School to Home

Stroke description to guide letter formation at home:

Pull down straight. Lift. Slide right. Lift. Slide right; stop short. Lift. Slide right.

Directions: Discuss the picture on the page. Help children identify **E** in the words on the signs.

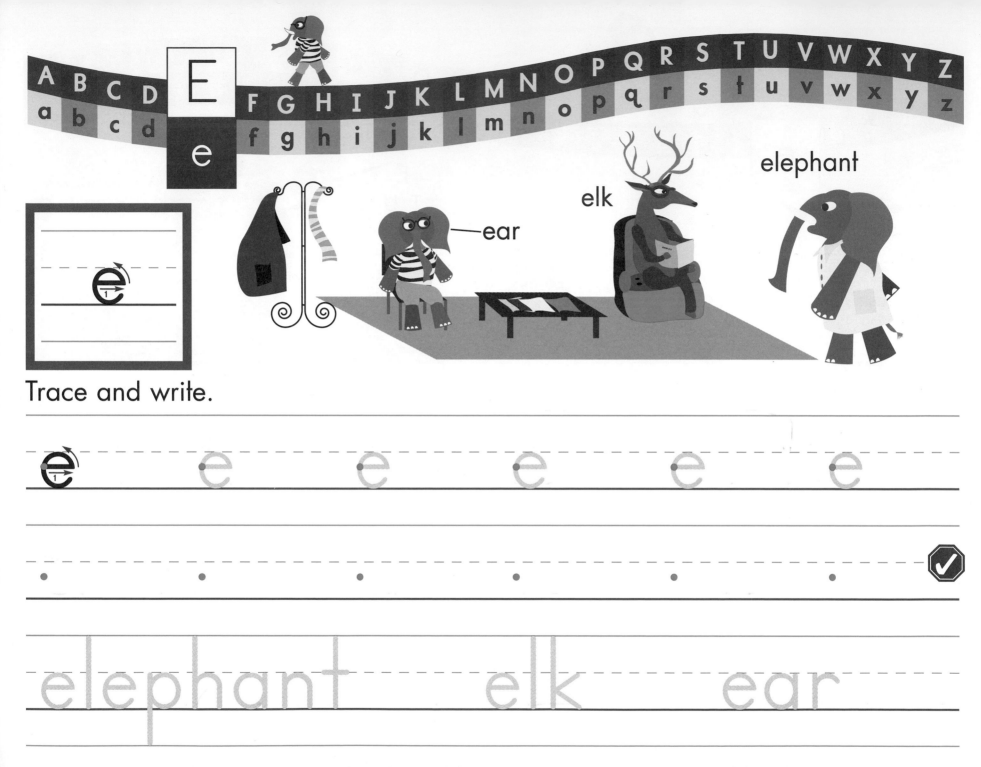

A B C D **E** F G H I J K L M N O P Q R S T U V W X Y Z
a b c d **e** f g h i j k l m n o p q r s t u v w x y z

ear

elk

elephant

Trace and write.

e e e e e e

· · · · · · · ✓

elephant elk ear

Stroke description to guide letter formation at home:

Slide right. Circle back.

e

Directions: Discuss the picture on the page. Help children identify **e** in the words that name the pictures.

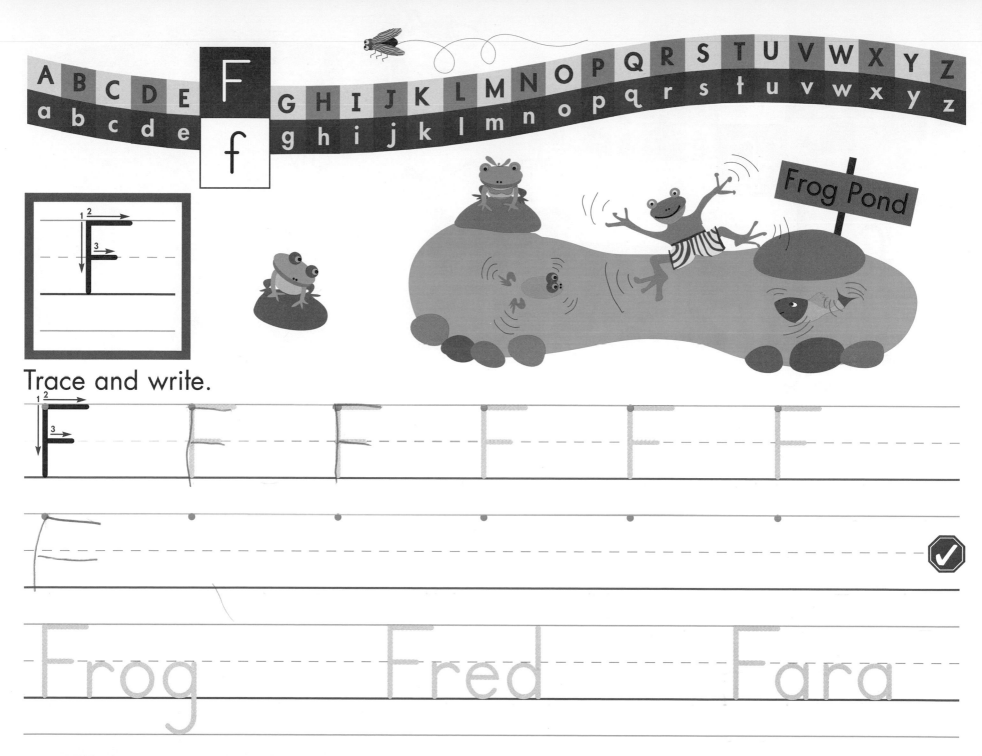

Frog Pond

Trace and write.

F   F   F   F   F   F   F

f

Frog   Fred   Fara

Stroke description to guide letter formation at home:

Pull down straight. Lift. Slide right. Lift.
Slide right; stop short.

Directions: Discuss the picture on the page.
Help children identify **F** in the words on
the sign.

A B C D E **F** G H I J K L M N O P Q R S T U V W X Y Z
a b c d e **f** g h i j k l m n o p q r s t u v w x y z

flute

fly

fish

Trace and write.

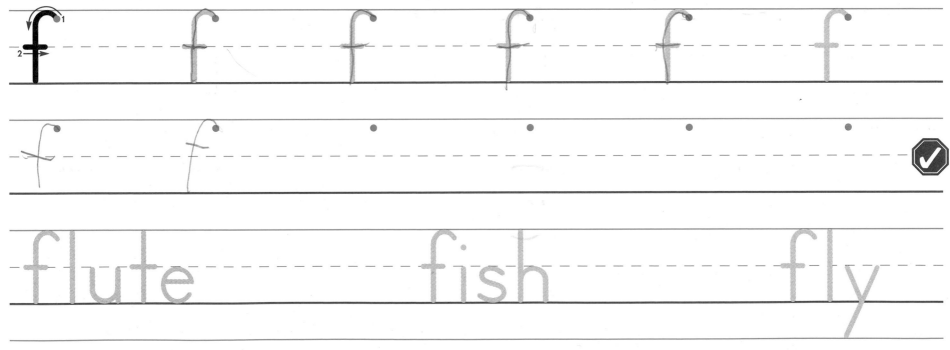

flute   fish   fly

Stroke description to guide letter formation at home:

Curve back; pull down straight.
Lift. Slide right.

Directions: Discuss the picture on the page. Help children identify **f** in the words that name the pictures.

School to Home

Practice

Write the letters.

c c

e e

f f

C C

E E

F F

Write the Alphabet

Write the missing uppercase letters.

B

G H   J

K   M N

P Q R S

U V W X Y Z

| A | B | C | D | E | F | G | H | I | J | K | L | M | N | O | P | Q | R | S | T | U | V | W | X | Y | Z |

| a | b | c | d | e | f | g | h | i | j | k | l | m | n | o | p | q | r | s | t | u | v | w | x | y | z |

Good night!

Trace and write.

G   G   G   G   G

G   G   G   G   G   ✓

Good   Gwen   Gus

School to Home

Stroke description to guide letter formation at home:

G — Circle back.
Slide left.

Directions: Discuss the picture on the page. Help children identify **G** in the words beside the pictures.

A B C D E F **G** H I J K L M N O P Q R S T U V W X Y Z
a b c d e f **g** h i j k l m n o p q r s t u v w x y z

garden

guitar

goat

Trace and write.

g g g g g g

g g g g g ✓

goat   guitar   garden

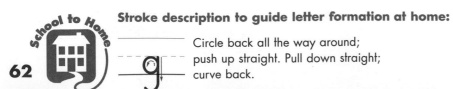

Stroke description to guide letter formation at home:

g | Circle back all the way around; push up straight. Pull down straight; curve back.

Directions: Discuss the picture on the page. Help children identify **g** in the words that name the pictures.

A B C D E F G H I **J** K L M N O P Q R S T U V W X Y Z
a b c d e f g h i **j** k l m n o p q r s t u v w x y z

Trace and write.

J J J J J J

J J J J J

Jack   Jill   Jug

Stroke description to guide letter formation at home:

School to Home

Pull down straight;
curve back. Lift. Slide right.

Directions: Discuss the picture on the page.
Help children identify **J** in the picture.

jam

juice

jar

Trace and write.

j j j j j j

j

jam   juice   jar

Stroke description to guide letter formation at home:

Pull down straight;
curve back. Lift. Dot.

Directions: Discuss the picture on the page. Help children identify **j** in the words that name the pictures.

School to Home

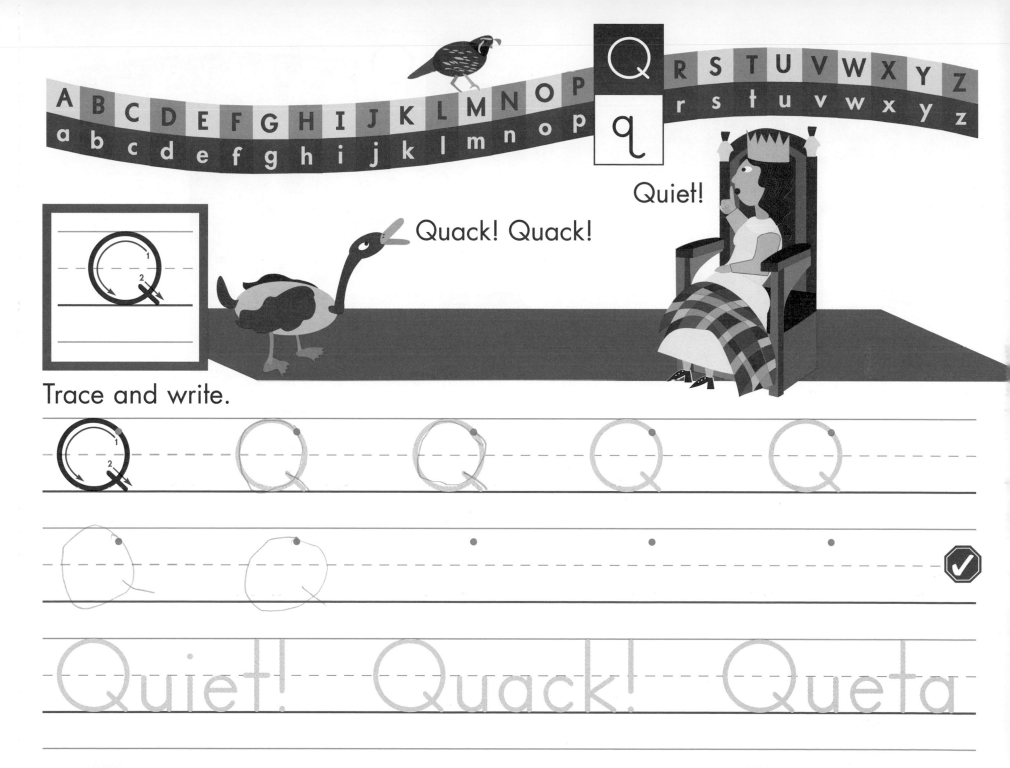

A B C D E F G H I J K L M N O P Q R S T U V W X Y Z
a b c d e f g h i j k l m n o p q r s t u v w x y z

Quiet!

Quack! Quack!

Trace and write.

Q Q Q Q Q

Quiet! Quack! Queta

Stroke description to guide letter formation at home:

Circle back all the way around. Lift. Slant right.

School to Home

Directions: Discuss the picture on the page. Help children identify **Q** in the words beside the pictures.

A B C D E F G H I J K L M N O P Q R S T U V W X Y Z
a b c d e f g h i j k l m n o p q r s t u v w x y z

queen

quail

quilt

Trace and write.

q q q q q q

q q q q ✓

queen   quail   quilt

School to Home

Stroke description to guide letter formation at home:

Circle back all the way around;
push up straight. Pull down straight;
curve forward.

Directions: Discuss the picture on the page. Help children identify **q** in the words that name the pictures.

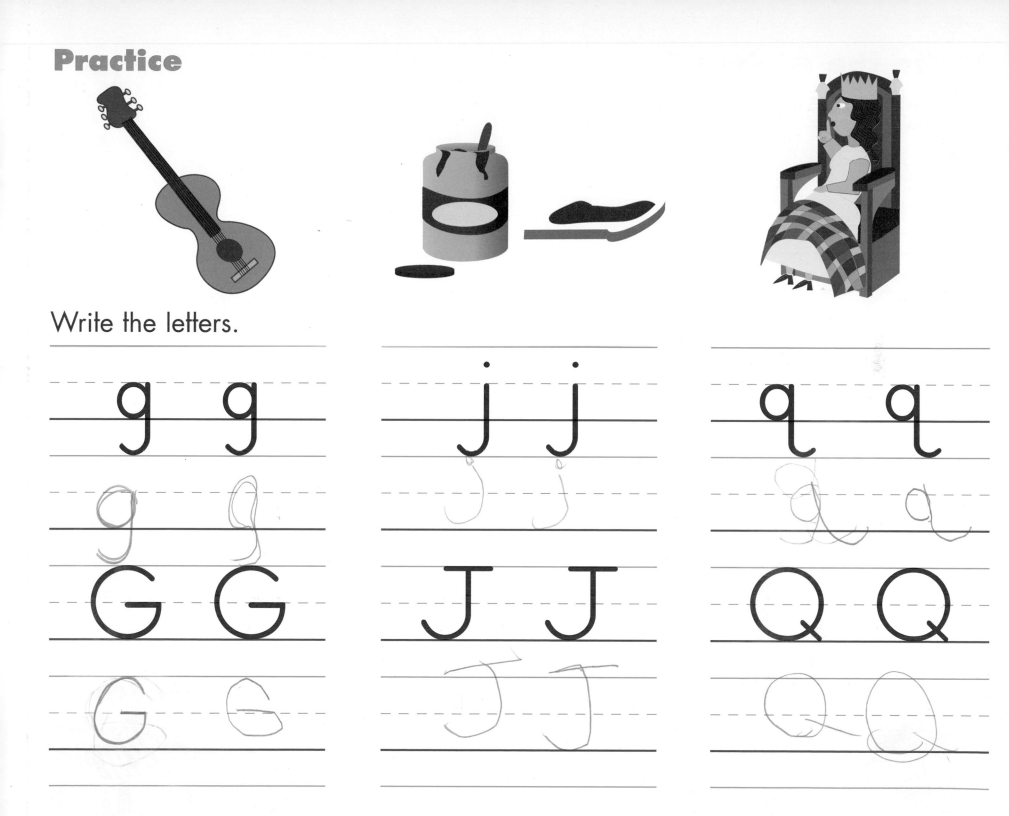

Write the letters.

g g

j j

q q

G G

J J

Q Q

Write the Alphabet

Write the missing lowercase letters.

b

h

k   m   n

p   r   s

u   v   w   x   y   z

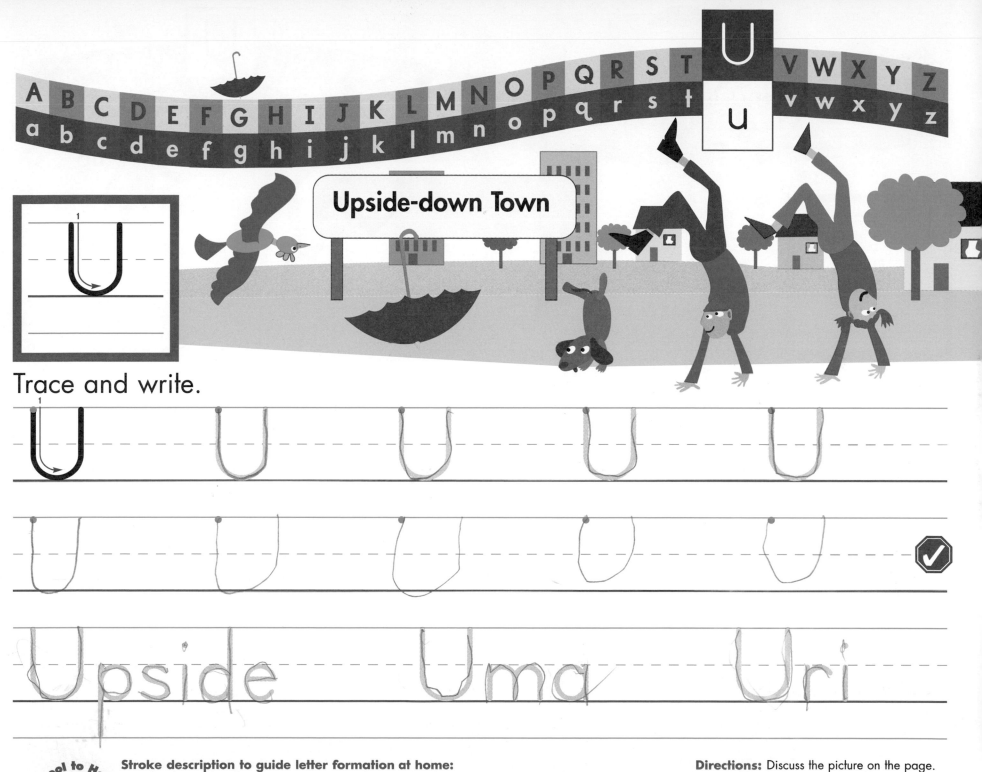

ABCDEFGHIJKLMNOPQRSTUVWXYZ
abcdefghijklmnopqrstuvwxyz

U u

Upside-down Town

Trace and write.

U U U U U

U U U U U

Upside   Uma   Uri

Stroke description to guide letter formation at home:

Pull down straight;
curve forward; push up.

Directions: Discuss the picture on the page.
Help children identify **U** in the words
on the sign.

69

A B C D E F G H I J K L M N O P Q R S T **U** V W X Y Z
a b c d e f g h i j k l m n o p q r s t **u** v w x y z

umbrella

up

under

Trace and write.

u u u u u u

u u u u u u ✓

umbrella   up   under

School to Home

Stroke description to guide letter formation at home:

Pull down straight;
curve forward; push up.
Pull down straight.

Directions: Discuss the picture on the page.
Help children identify **u** in the words that name
the pictures.

Trace and write.

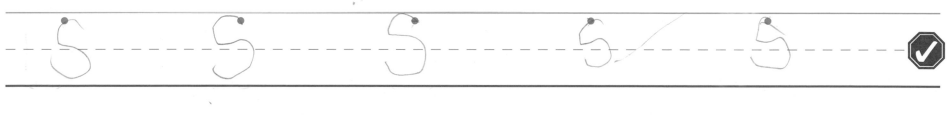

Stroke description to guide letter formation at home:

S Curve back;
curve forward.

Directions: Discuss the picture on the page.
Help children identify **S** in the words
on the signs.

swing

sun

slide

S

Trace and write.

S S S S S S

• • • • • • ✔

sun   slide   swing

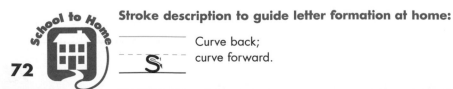

Stroke description to guide letter formation at home:

Curve back;
curve forward.

72

Directions: Discuss the picture on the page. Help children identify **s** in the words that name the pictures.

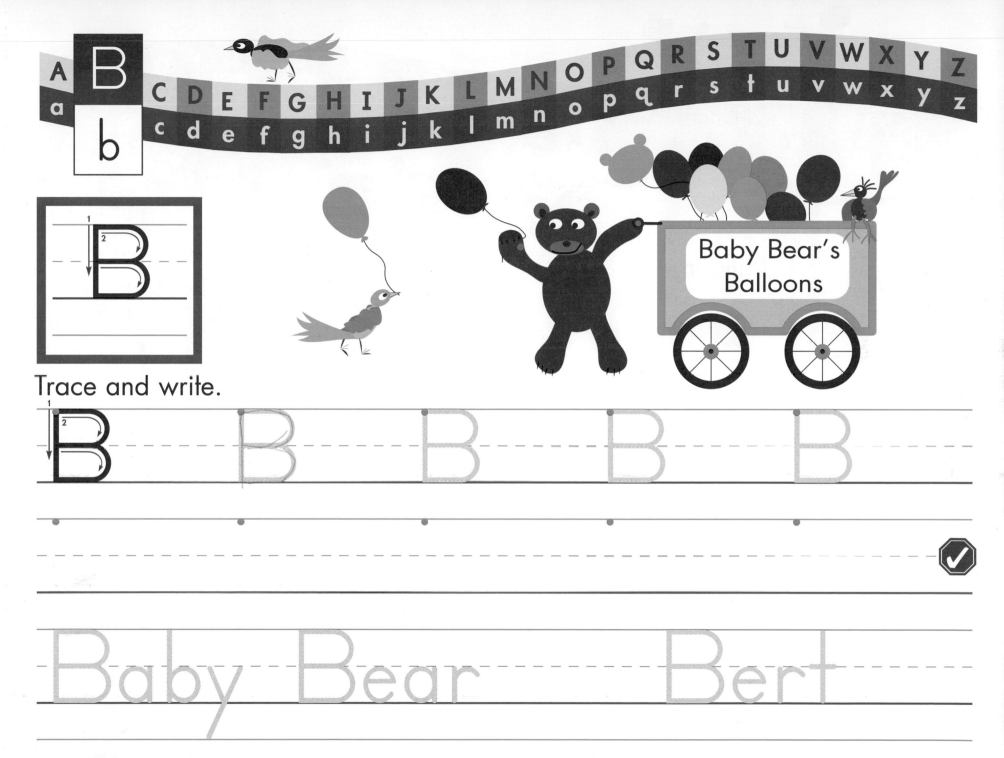

A B a
b

A C D E F G H I J K L M N O P Q R S T U V W X Y Z
C D E F G H I J K L M N O P Q R S T U V W X Y Z
c d e f g h i j k l m n o p q r s t u v w x y z

Baby Bear's Balloons

Trace and write.

B   B   B   B   B

Baby Bear   Bert

School to Home

Stroke description to guide letter formation at home:

B   Pull down straight. Lift. Slide right;
curve forward; slide left. Slide right;
curve forward; slide left.

Directions: Discuss the picture on the page.
Help children identify **B** in the words on
the sign.

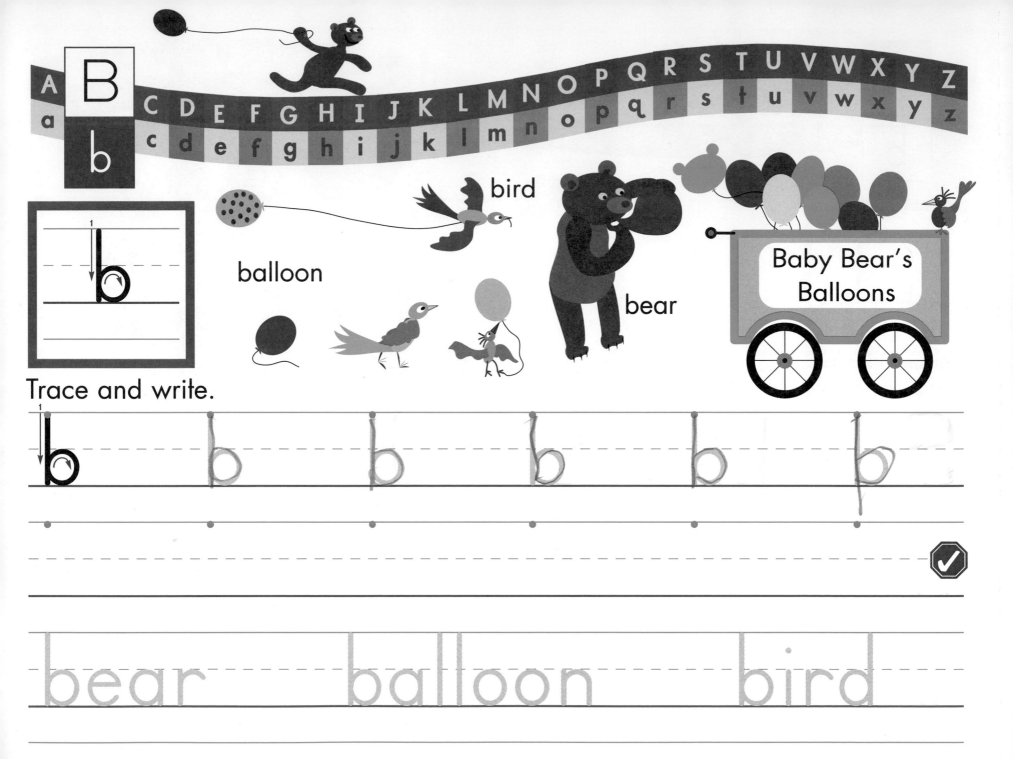

B / b

A a

A	B	C	D	E	F	G	H	I	J	K	L	M	N	O	P	Q	R	S	T	U	V	W	X	Y	Z
a	b	c	d	e	f	g	h	i	j	k	l	m	n	o	p	q	r	s	t	u	v	w	x	y	z

balloon

bird

bear

Baby Bear's Balloons

Trace and write.

b   b   b   b   b   b   b

bear   balloon   bird

School to Home

Stroke description to guide letter formation at home:

b Pull down straight;
push up. Circle forward.

Directions: Discuss the picture on the page. Help children identify **b** in the words that name the pictures.

A B C D E F G H I J K L M N O **P** Q R S T U V W X Y Z
a b c d e f g h i j k l m n o **p** q r s t u v w x y z

Pet Store

Trace and write.

P   P   P   P   P   P

P e t   P a m   P e t e

Stroke description to guide letter formation at home:

School to Home

Pull down straight. Lift.
Slide right; curve forward;
slide left.

Directions: Discuss the picture on the page.
Help children identify **P** in the words
on the sign.

75

poodle

parrot

pig

Trace and write.

p p p p p p ✓

pig parrot poodle

Stroke description to guide letter formation at home:

Pull down straight.
Push up. Circle forward
all the way around.

p

Directions: Discuss the picture on the page. Help children identify **p** in the words that name the pictures.

76

Write the letters.

u u s s b b p p

U U S S B B P P

Write the Alphabet

Write the missing uppercase letters.

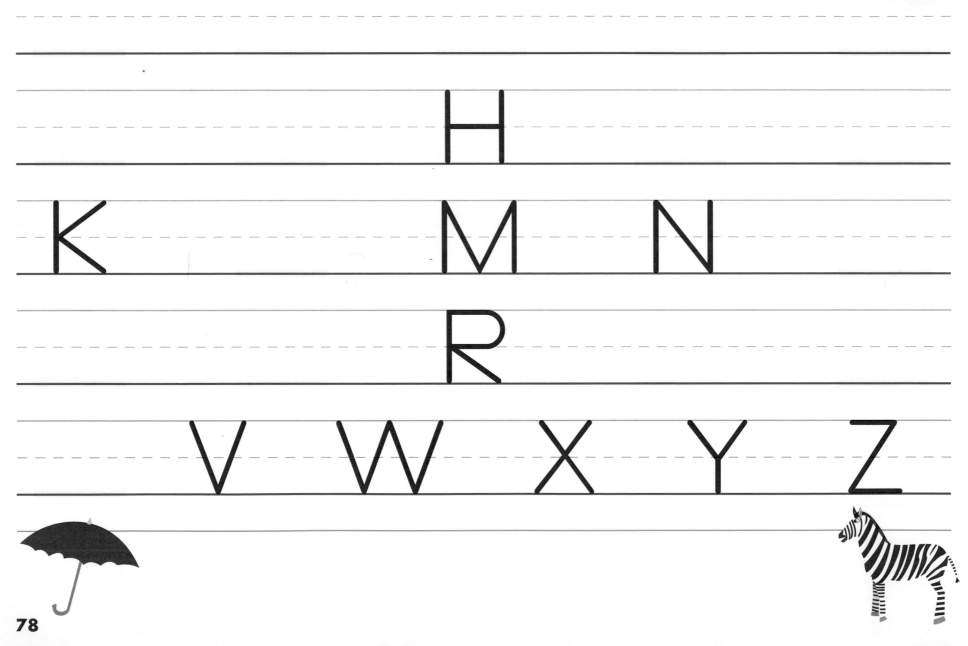

H

K   M   N

R

V   W   X   Y   Z

R
r

A B C D E F G H I J K L M N O P Q R S T U V W X Y Z
a b c d e f g h i j k l m n o p q r s t u v w x y z

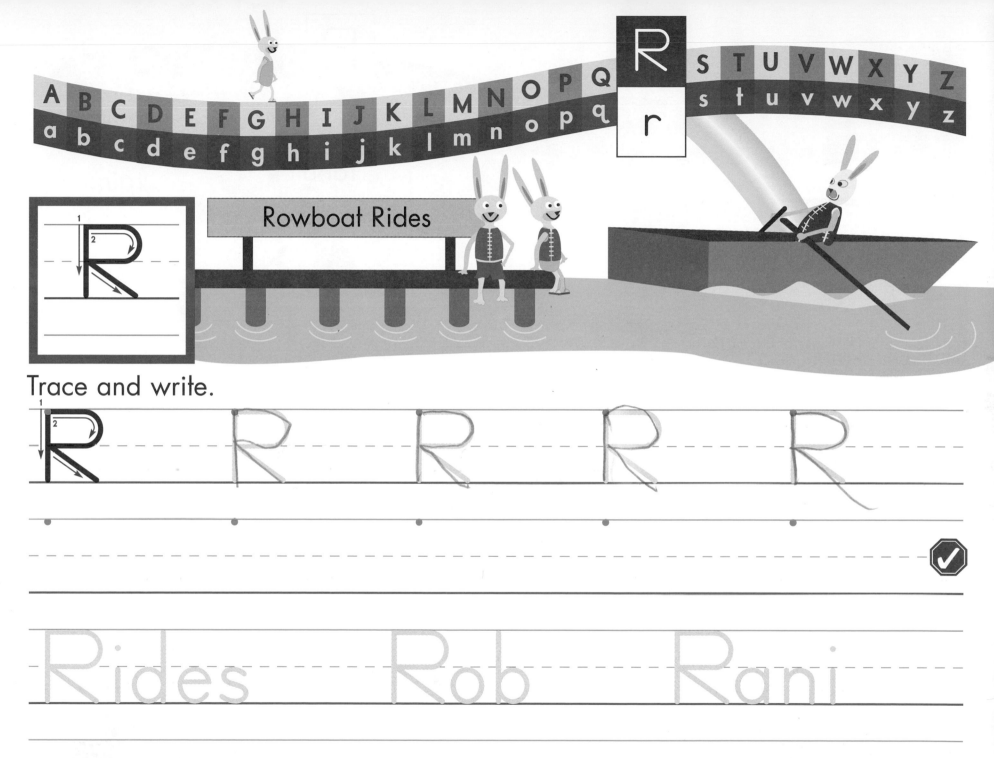

Rowboat Rides

Trace and write.

R   R   R   R   R

Rides   Rob   Rani

Stroke description to guide letter formation at home:

R
Pull down straight. Lift.
Slide right; curve forward; slide left.
Slant right.

Directions: Discuss the picture on the page.
Help children identify **R** in the words
on the sign.

79

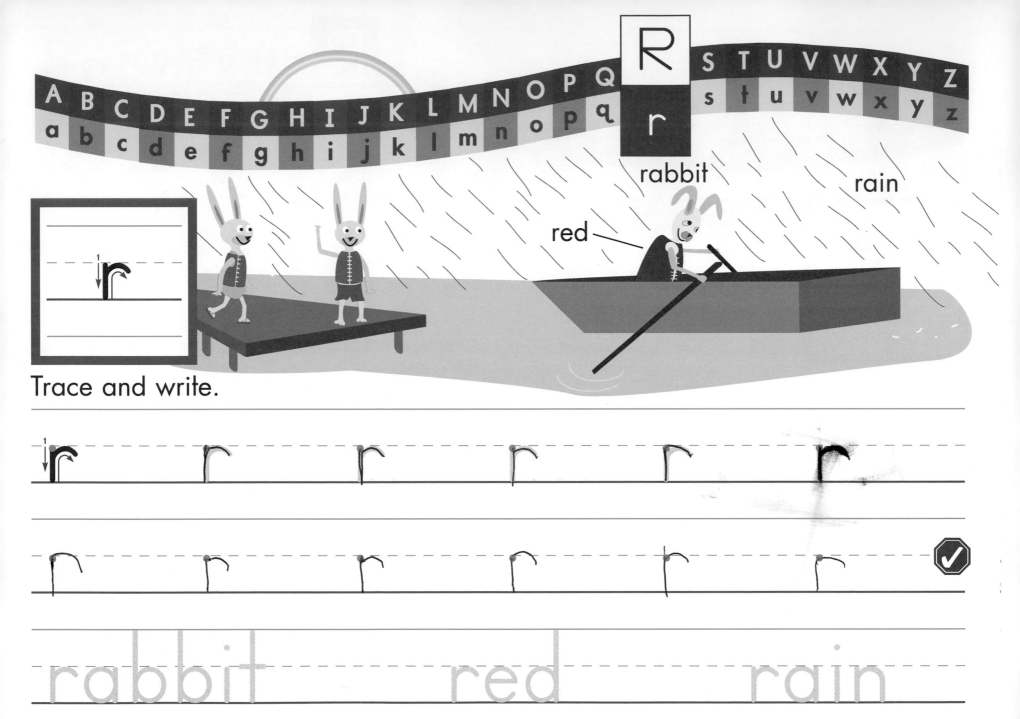

A B C D E F G H I J K L M N O P Q **R** S T U V W X Y Z
a b c d e f g h i j k l m n o p q **r** s t u v w x y z

rabbit

red

rain

Trace and write.

r r r r r r

r r r r r r ✓

rabbit red rain

Stroke description to guide letter formation at home:

School to Home

Pull down straight. Push up;
curve forward.

80

Directions: Discuss the picture on the page. Help children identify **r** in the words that name the pictures.

A B C D E F G H I J K L M **N** O P Q R S T U V W X Y Z

a b c d e f g h i j k l m **n** o p q r s t u v w x y z

Trace and write.

N N N N N

N W U W N ✓

News Nick Nancy

Stroke description to guide letter formation at home:

School to Home

Pull down straight. Lift.
Slant right. Push up straight.

Directions: Discuss the picture on the page.
Help children identify **N** in the picture.

81

A B C D E F G H I J K L M **N** O P Q R S T U V W X Y Z
a b c d e f g h i j k l m **n** o p q r s t u v w x y z

numbers

nest

nine

Trace and write.

n   n   n   n   n   n

numbers   nest   nine

Stroke description to guide letter formation at home:

Pull down straight. Push up;
curve forward; pull down straight.

Directions: Discuss the picture on the page. Help children identify **n** in the words that name the pictures.

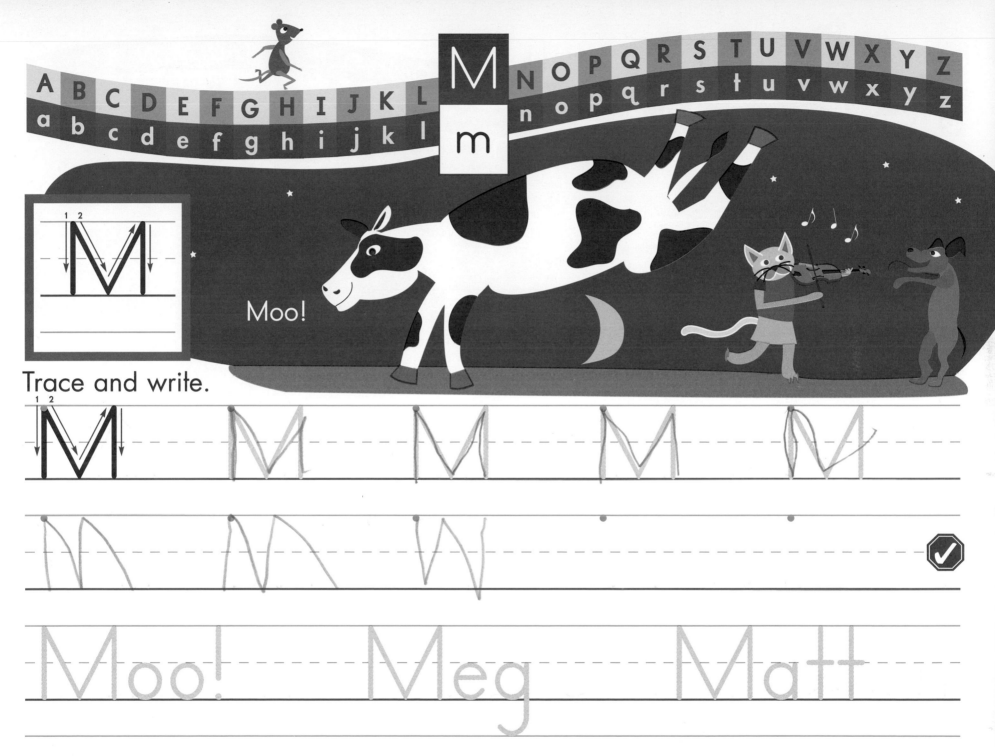

Moo!

Trace and write.

M M M M M M M

M M W

Moo! Meg Matt

Stroke description to guide letter formation at home:

Pull down straight. Lift. Slant right.
Slant up. Pull down straight.

Directions: Discuss the picture on the page.
Help children identify **M** in the picture.

A B C D E F G H I J K L **M** N O P Q R S T U V W X Y Z
a b c d e f g h i j k l **m** n o p q r s t u v w x y z

moon

mouse

milk

Trace and write.

m m m m m m

m m m m m m ✓

milk mouse moon

School to Home

Stroke description to guide letter formation at home:

m Pull down straight. Push up; curve forward; pull down straight. Push up; curve forward; pull down straight.

Directions: Discuss the picture on the page. Help children identify **m** in the words that name the pictures.

A	B	C	D	E	F	G	H	I	J	K	L	M	N	O	P	Q	R	S	T	U	V	W	X	Y	Z
a	b	c	d	e	f	g	h	i	j	k	l	m	n	o	p	q	r	s	t	u	v	w	x	y	z

Happy Birthday Helen!

Trace and write.

Helen Hen Happy

Stroke description to guide letter formation at home:

Pull down straight. Lift.
Pull down straight. Lift. Slide right.

Directions: Discuss the picture on the page. Help children identify **H** in the words on the sign.

| A | B | | C | D | E | F | G | **H** | I | J | K | L | M | N | O | P | Q | R | S | T | U | V | W | X | Y | Z |
| a | b | | c | d | e | f | g | **h** | i | j | k | l | m | n | o | p | q | r | s | t | u | v | w | x | y | z |

hat

hill

hen

Trace and write.

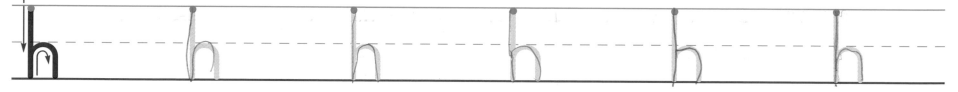

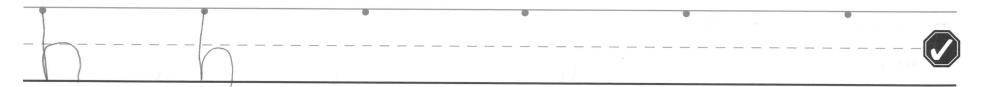

hen hat hill

School to Home

Stroke description to guide letter formation at home:

Pull down straight. Push up; curve forward; pull down straight.

86

Directions: Discuss the picture on the page. Help children identify **h** in the words that name the pictures.

Practice

Write the letters.

r r   n n   m m   h h

R R   N N   M M   H H

Write the Alphabet

Write the missing lowercase letters.

k

v   w   x   y   z

ABCDEFGHIJKLMNOPQRSTU V WXYZ
abcdefghijklmnopqrstu v wxyz

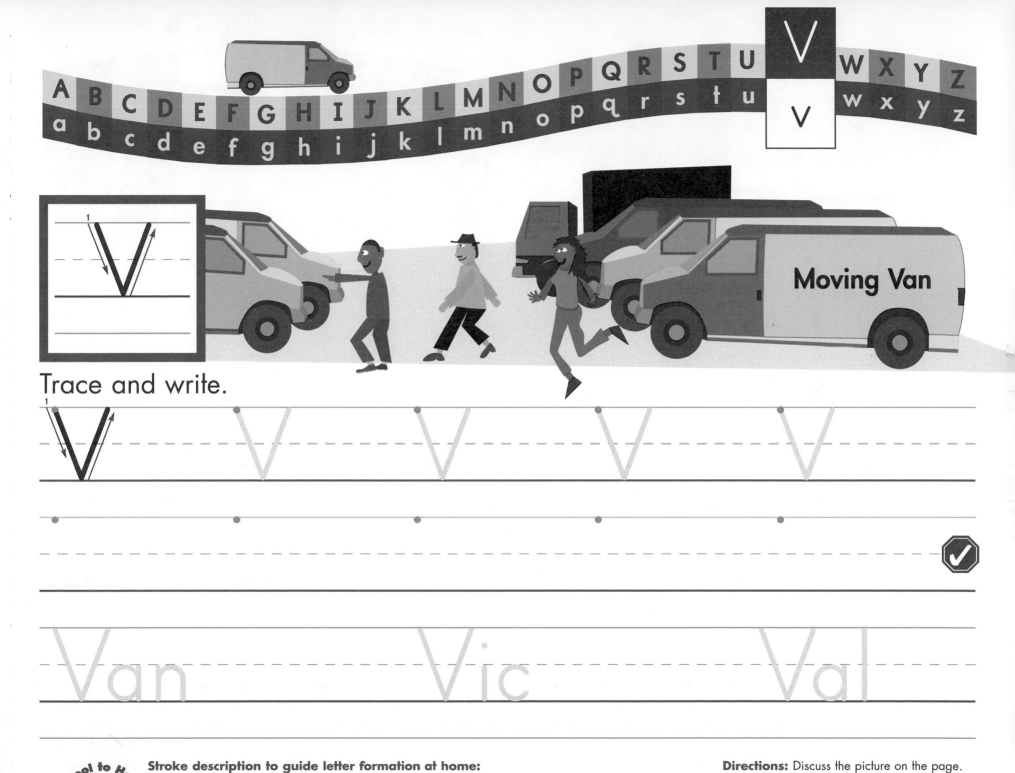

Moving Van

Trace and write.

V V V V V

Van   Vic   Val

School to Home

Stroke description to guide letter formation at home:

Slant right.
Slant up.

Directions: Discuss the picture on the page.
Help children identify **V** in the picture.

89

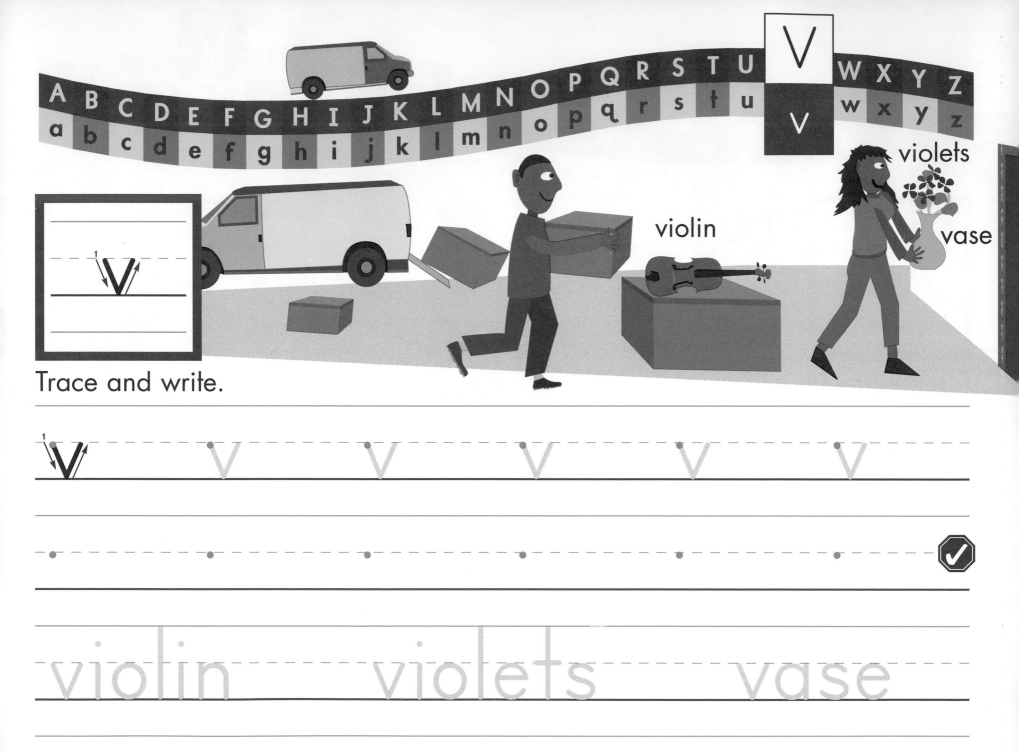

A B C D E F G H I J K L M N O P Q R S T U V W X Y Z

a b c d e f g h i j k l m n o p q r s t u v w x y z

violin

violets

vase

Trace and write.

V v v v v v v v v

violin   violets   vase

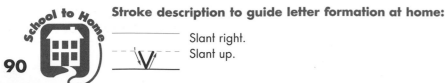

Stroke description to guide letter formation at home:

School to Home

Slant right.
Slant up.

Directions: Discuss the picture on the page. Help children identify **v** in the words that name the pictures.

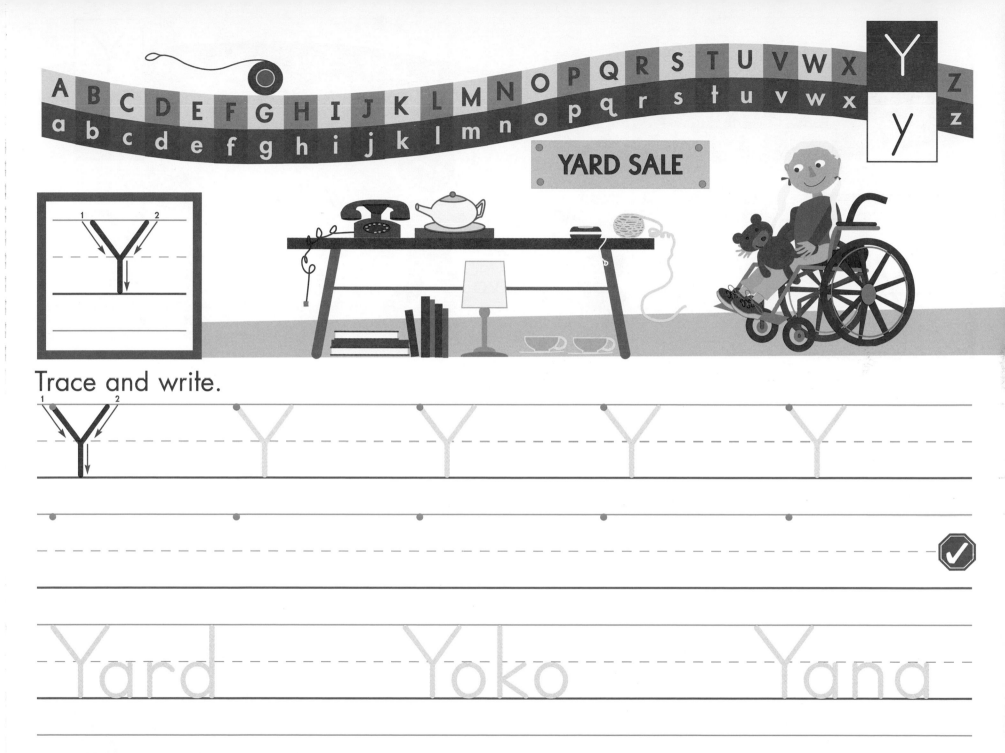

A B C D E F G H I J K L M N O P Q R S T U V W X Y Z
a b c d e f g h i j k l m n o p q r s t u v w x y z

YARD SALE

Y
y

Trace and write.

Y   Y   Y   Y   Y   Y

✓

Yard   Yoko   Yana

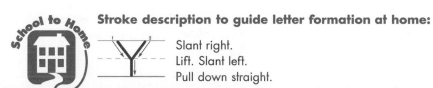

Stroke description to guide letter formation at home:

Slant right.
Lift. Slant left.
Pull down straight.

Directions: Discuss the picture on the page.
Help children identify **Y** in the words on the sign.

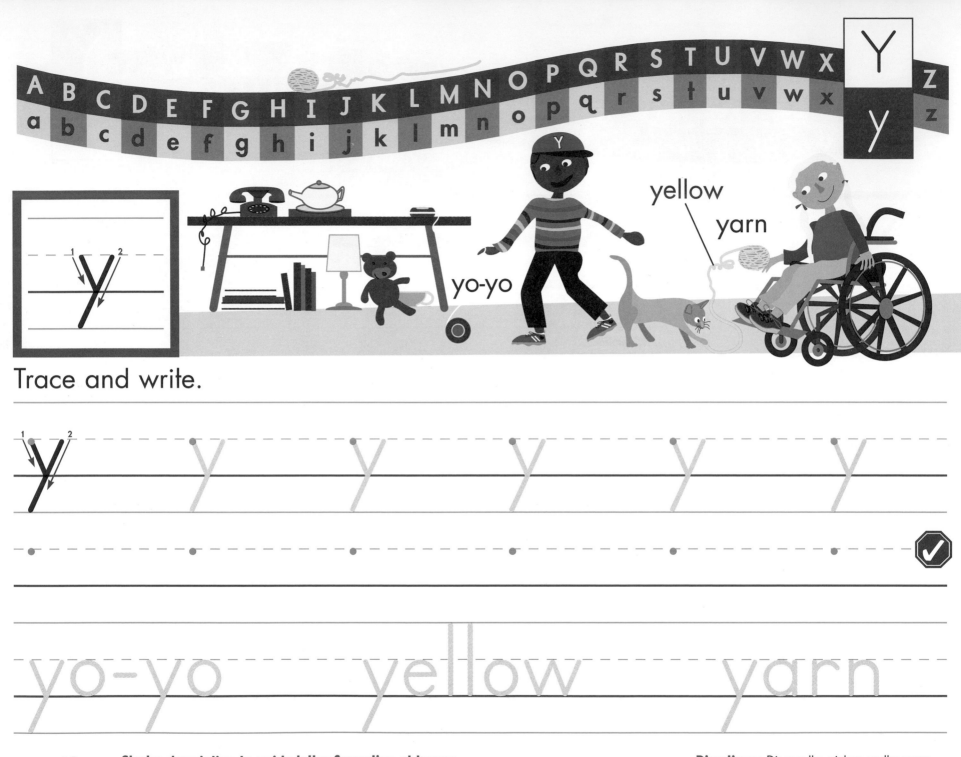

yellow
yarn
yo-yo

Trace and write.

y   y   y   y   y   y   y ✓

yo-yo   yellow   yarn

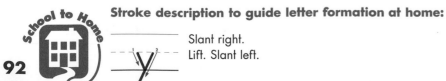

Stroke description to guide letter formation at home:

Slant right.
Lift. Slant left.

92

Directions: Discuss the picture on the page. Help children identify **y** in the words that name the pictures.

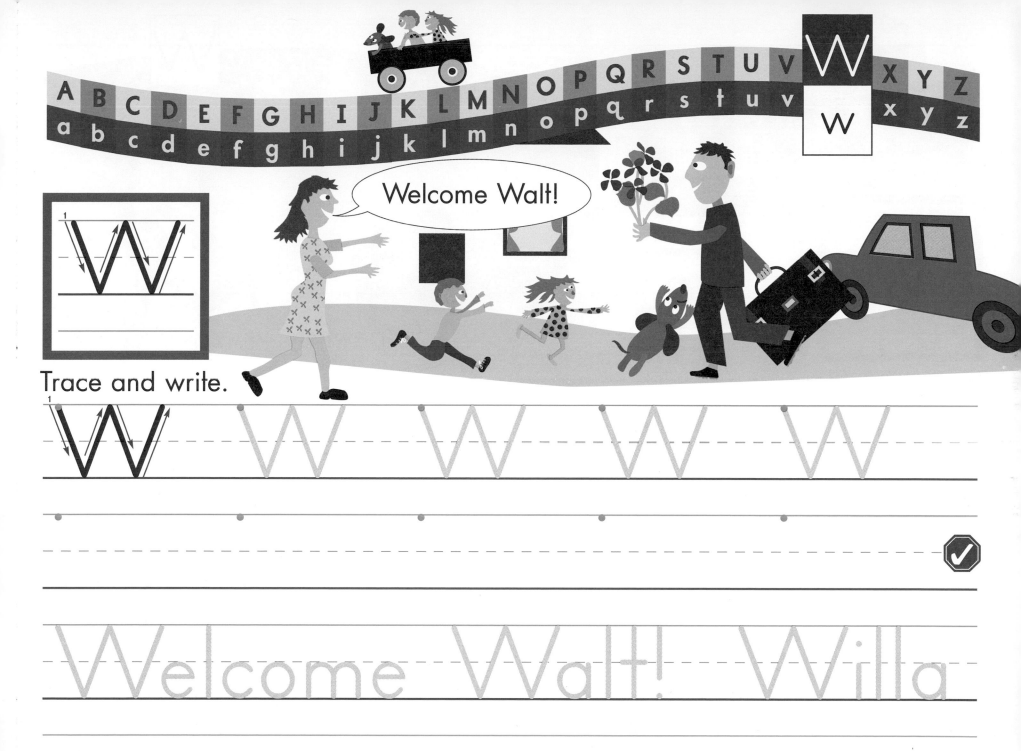

A B C D E F G H I J K L M N O P Q R S T U V **W** X Y Z
a b c d e f g h i j k l m n o p q r s t u v **w** x y z

Welcome Walt!

Trace and write.

W W W W W W

Welcome Walt! Willa

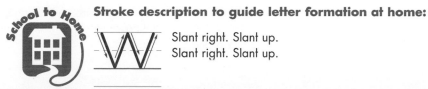

Stroke description to guide letter formation at home:

Slant right. Slant up.
Slant right. Slant up.

Directions: Discuss the picture on the page. Help children identify **W** in the picture.

A B C D E F G H I J K L M N O P Q R S T U V W X Y Z
a b c d e f g h i j k l m n o p q r s t u v w x y z

W
W

window

wagon

wheel

Trace and write.

W W W W W W

wagon wheel window

School to Home

Stroke description to guide letter formation at home:

Slant right. Slant up.
Slant right. Slant up.

Directions: Discuss the picture on the page. Help children identify **w** in the words that name the pictures.

Practice

Write the letters.

v   v   y   y   w   w

V   V   Y   Y   W   W

Write the Alphabet

Write the missing uppercase letters.

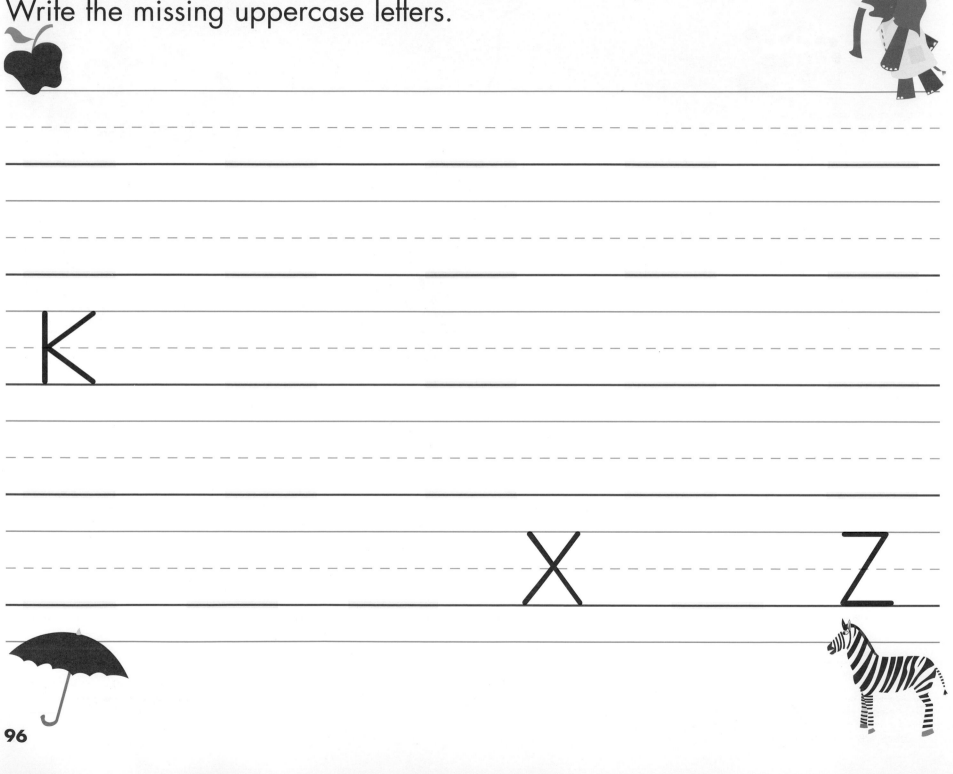

K

X   Z

A B C D E F G H I J K L M N O P Q R S T U V W X Y Z
a b c d e f g h i j k l m n o p q r s t u v w x y z

EXIT

Trace and write.

X   X   X   X   X

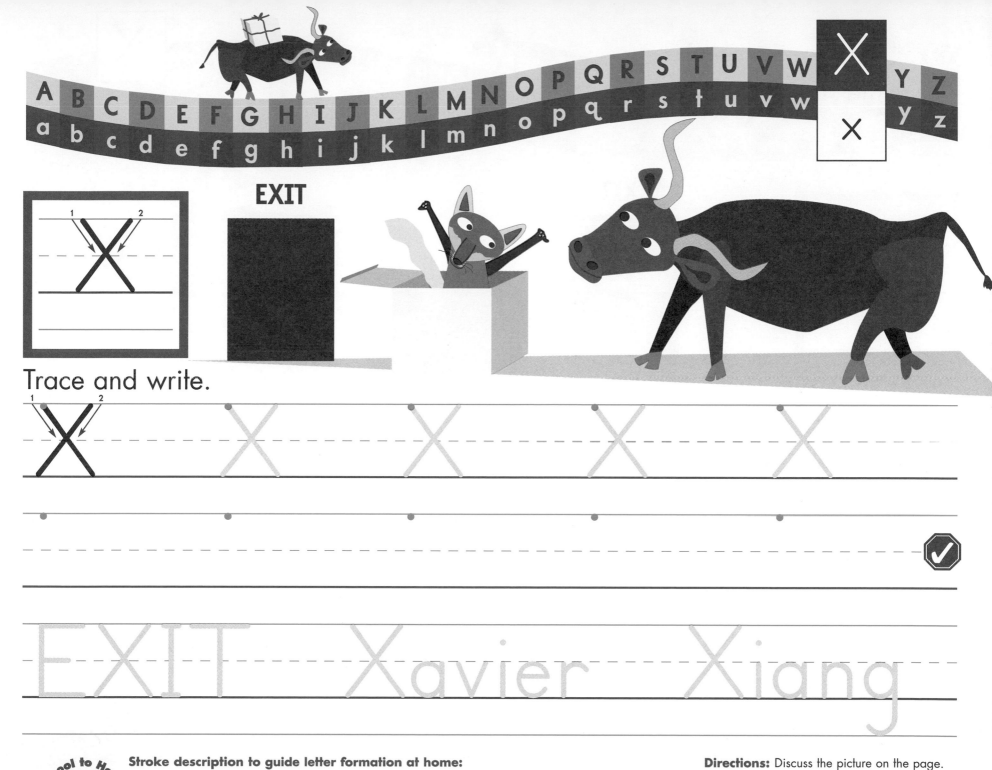

EXIT   Xavier   Xiang

School to Home

Stroke description to guide letter formation at home:
Slant right.
Lift. Slant left.

Directions: Discuss the picture on the page. Help children identify **X** on the sign.

A B C D E F G H I J K L M N O P Q R S T U V W X Y Z
a b c d e f g h i j k l m n o p q r s t u v w x y z

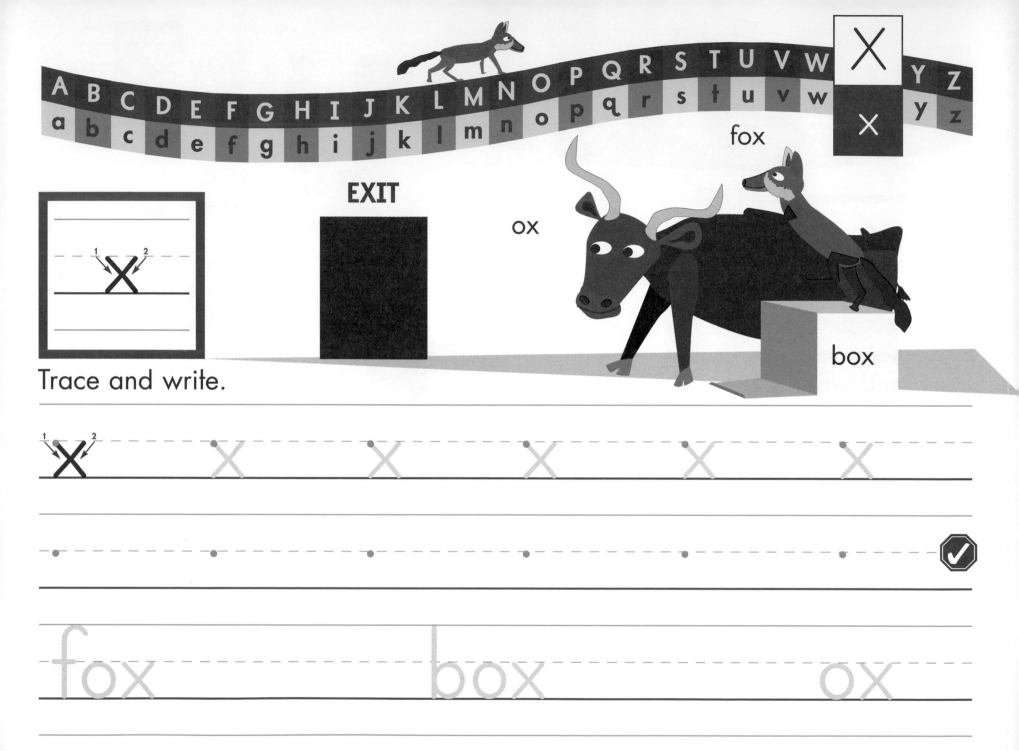

X

EXIT

fox

ox

box

Trace and write.

1 → X ← 2   X   X   X   X   X

✓

fox   box   ox

School to Home

98

Stroke description to guide letter formation at home:

Slant right.
Lift. Slant left.

1 → X ← 2

Directions: Discuss the picture on the page. Help children identify **x** in the words that name the pictures.

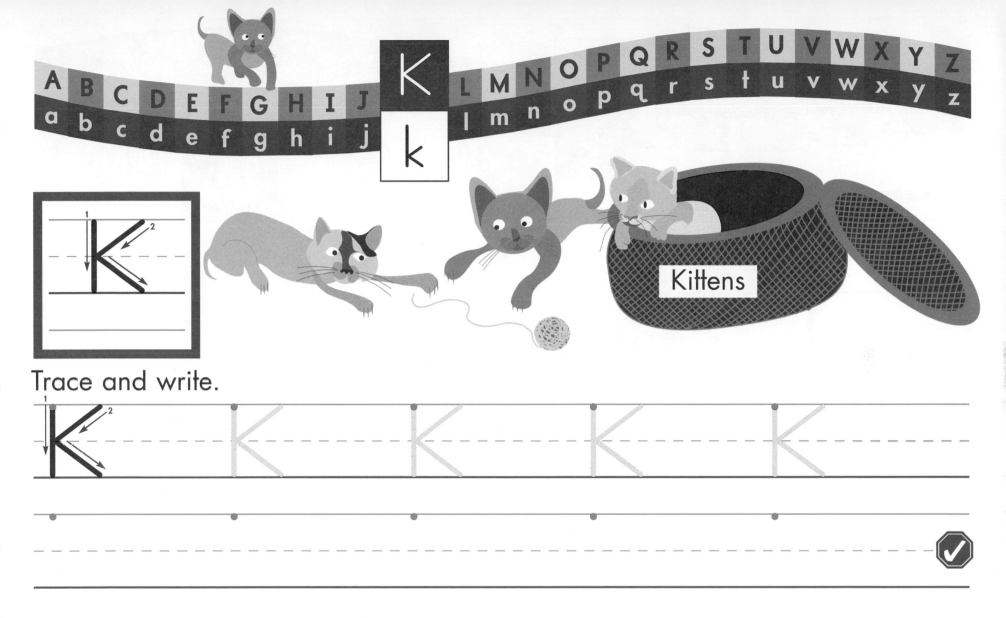

A B C D E F G H I J K L M N O P Q R S T U V W X Y Z
a b c d e f g h i j k l m n o p q r s t u v w x y z

K
k

Kittens

Trace and write.

K K K K K

✓

Kittens   Kate   Ken

Stroke description to guide letter formation at home:

K Pull down straight.
Lift. Slant left. Slant right.

Directions: Discuss the picture on the page.
Help children identify **K** on the sign.

99

A B C D E F G H I J K L M N O P Q R S T U V W X Y Z
a b c d e f g h i j k l m n o p q r s t u v w x y z

K
k

kite   key   king

Trace and write.

k   k   k   k   k   k   k

✔

kite   key   king

School to Home

100

Stroke description to guide letter formation at home:

Pull down straight. Lift.
Slant left. Slant right.

Directions: Discuss the picture on the page. Help children identify **k** in the words that name the pictures.

A B C D E F G H I J K L M N O P Q R S T U V W X Y
a b c d e f g h i j k l m n o p q r s t u v w x y

Z
z

Zoom! Zoom!

Z

Trace and write.

Z   Z   Z   Z   Z

Zoom!   Zara   Zack

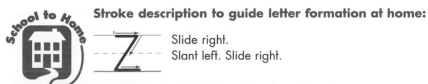

Stroke description to guide letter formation at home:

Z   Slide right.
     Slant left. Slide right.

Directions: Discuss the picture on the page. Help children identify **Z** in the words beside the pictures.

101

A B C D E F G H I J K L M N O P Q R S T U V W X Y Z
a b c d e f g h i j k l m n o p q r s t u v w x y z

zebra

zero

zipper

Trace and write.

z   z   z   z   z   z   z

zebra   zero   zipper

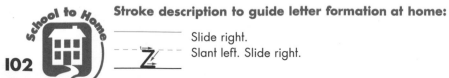

Stroke description to guide letter formation at home:

Slide right.
Slant left. Slide right.

Directions: Discuss the picture on the page.
Help children identify **z** in the words that name
the pictures.

Practice

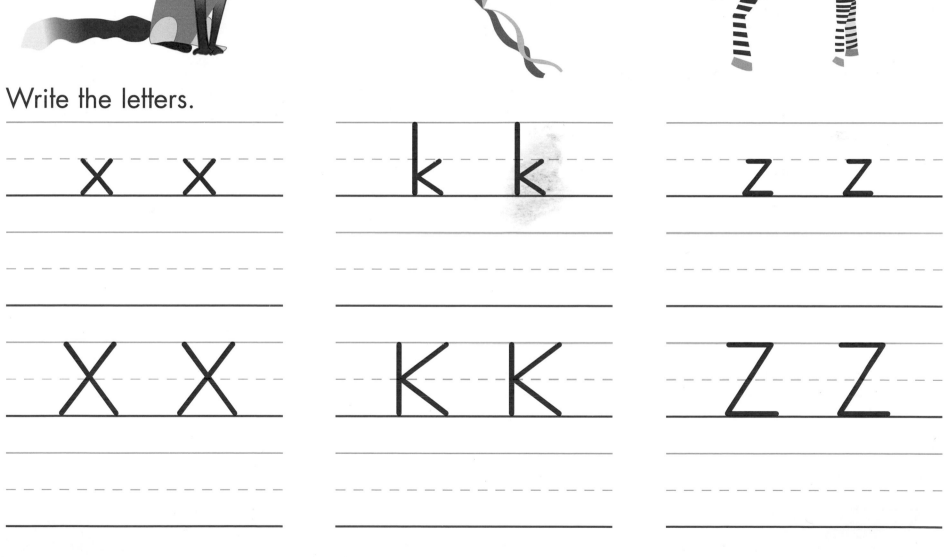

Write the letters.

x   x

k   k

z   z

X   X

K   K

Z   Z

Write the Alphabet

Write the lowercase alphabet.

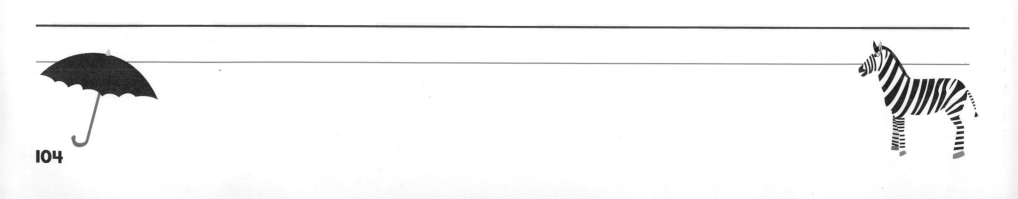

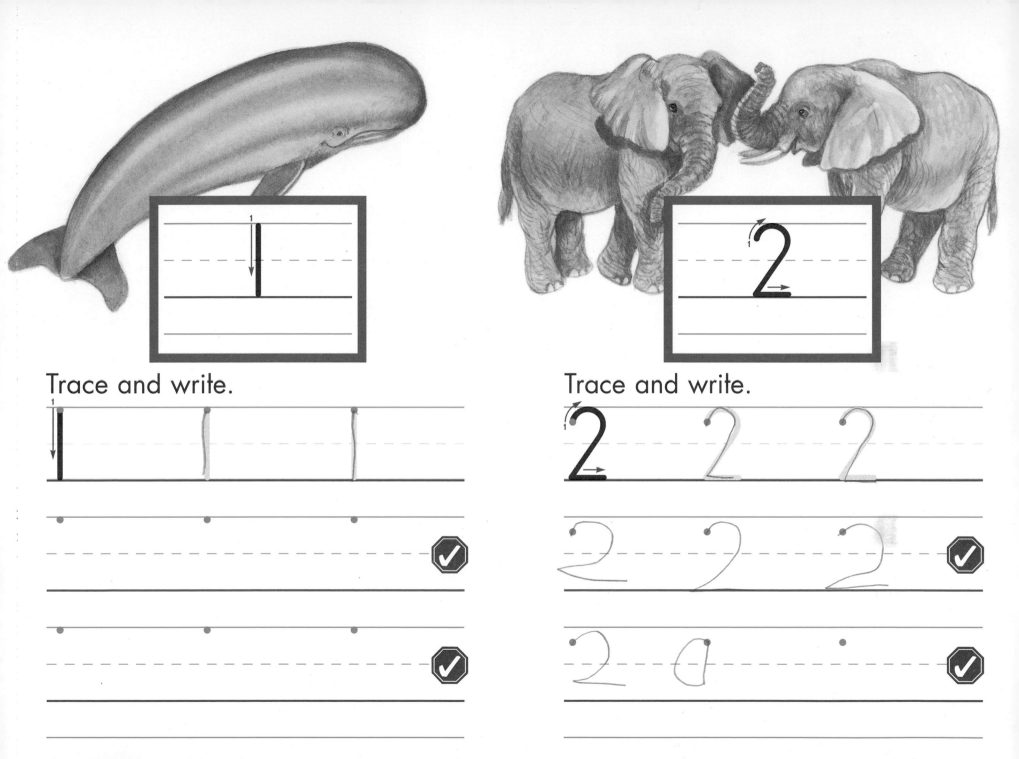

Trace and write.

Trace and write.

Trace and write.

3   3   3

✔

✔

Trace and write.

4   4   4

✔

✔

School to Home

Stroke descriptions to guide numeral formation at home:

3   Curve forward. Curve forward.

4   Pull down straight. Slide right. Lift.
    Pull down straight.

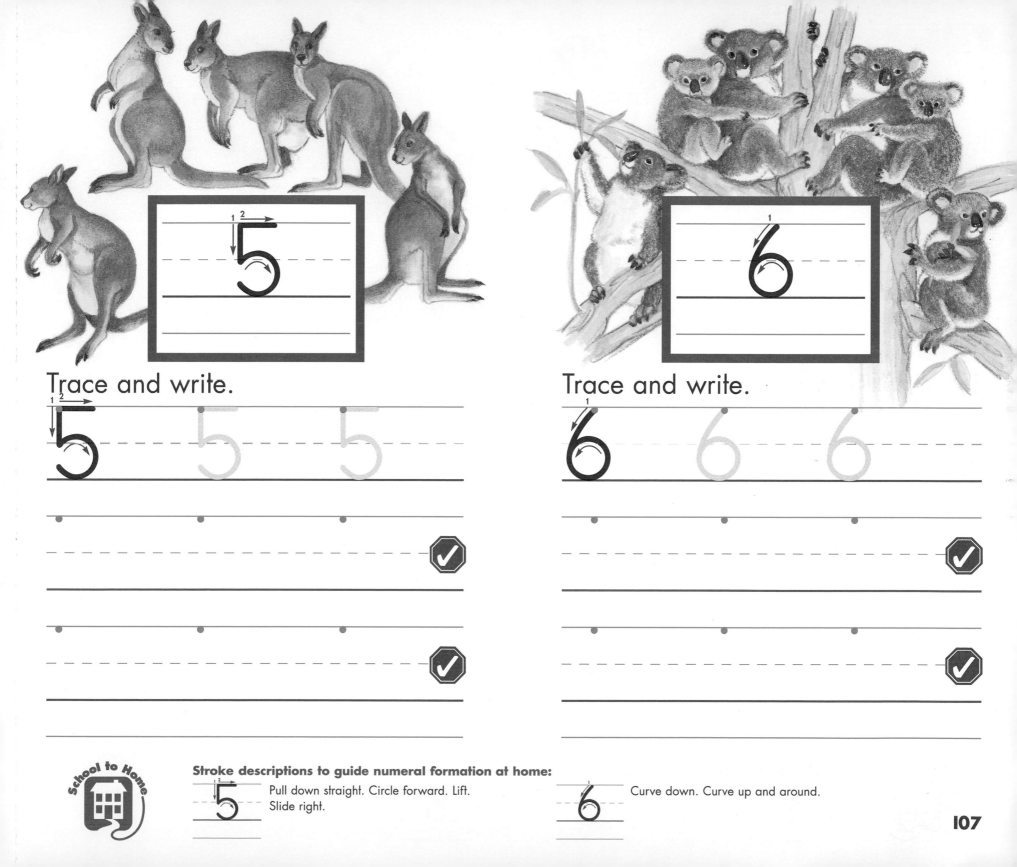

Trace and write.

5   5   5   ✔

✔

Trace and write.

6   6   6   ✔

✔

Stroke descriptions to guide numeral formation at home:

5 Pull down straight. Circle forward. Lift. Slide right.

6 Curve down. Curve up and around.

107

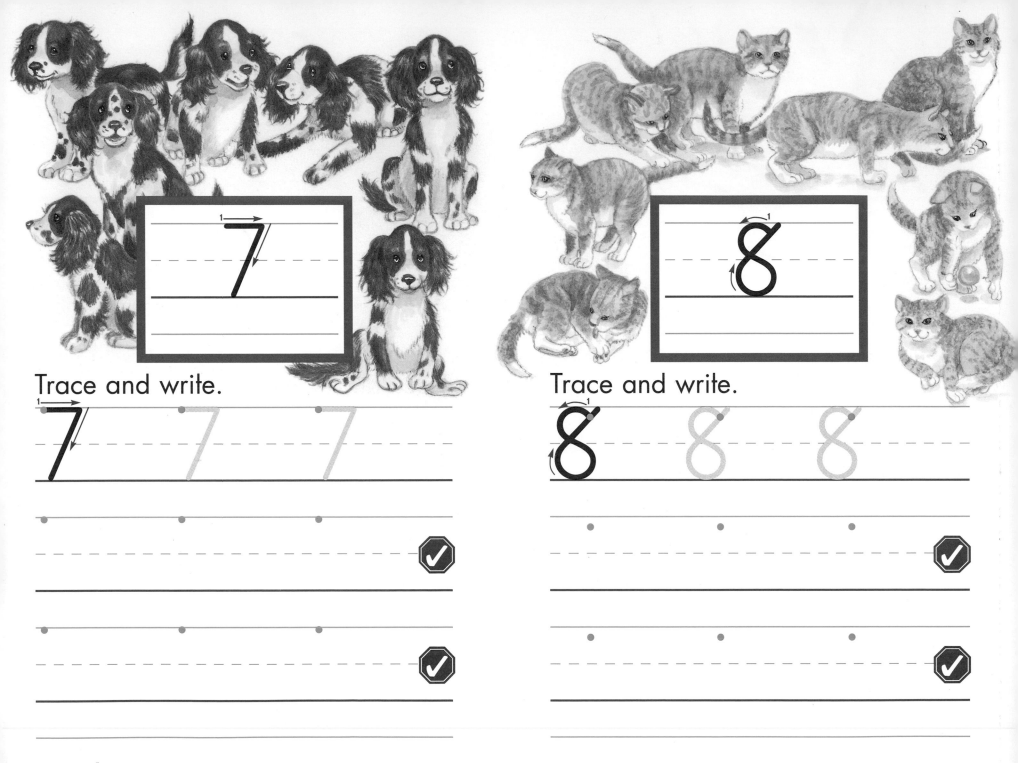

7

Trace and write.

7 7 7

✔

✔

Trace and write.

8 8 8

✔

✔

Stroke descriptions to guide numeral formation at home:

7 Slide right. Slant left.

 8 Curve back; curve forward. Slant up.

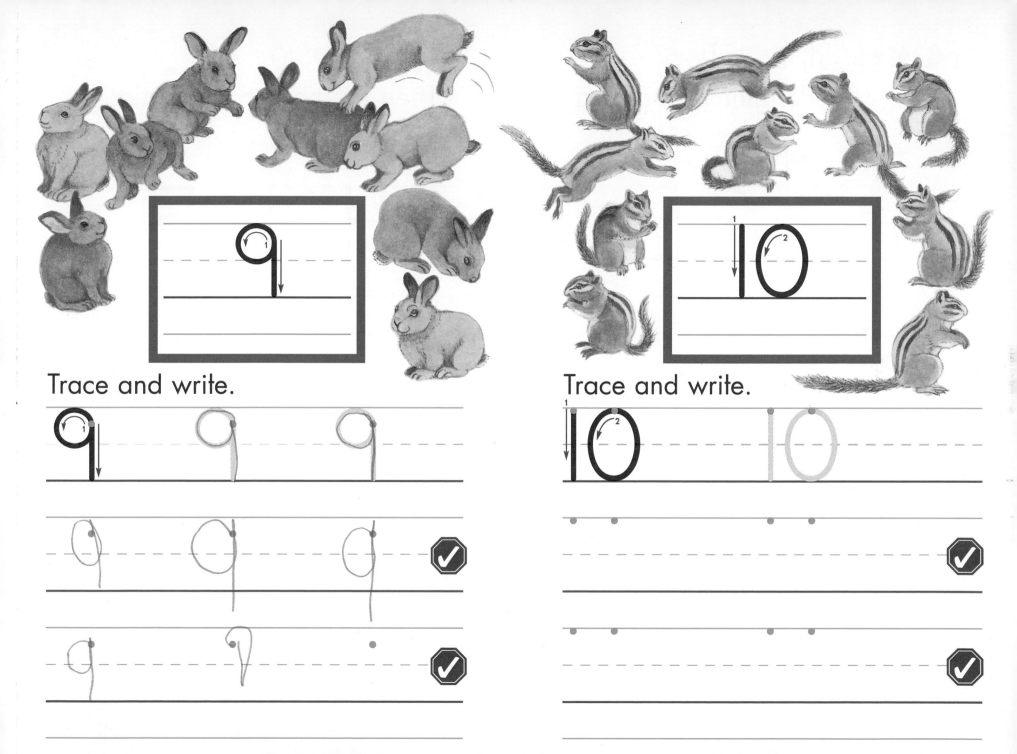

Trace and write.

Trace and write.

Stroke descriptions to guide numeral formation at home:

 Circle back all the way around.
Pull down straight.

Pull down straight. Lift. Curve down; curve up.

109

Practice   1, 2, 3, 4, 5   6, 7, 8, 9, 10

Penguins jump and dive.   Then up they come again.

Trace and write.

1   2   3   4   5

6   7   8   9   10

Write Numerals

How many? Write the numeral.

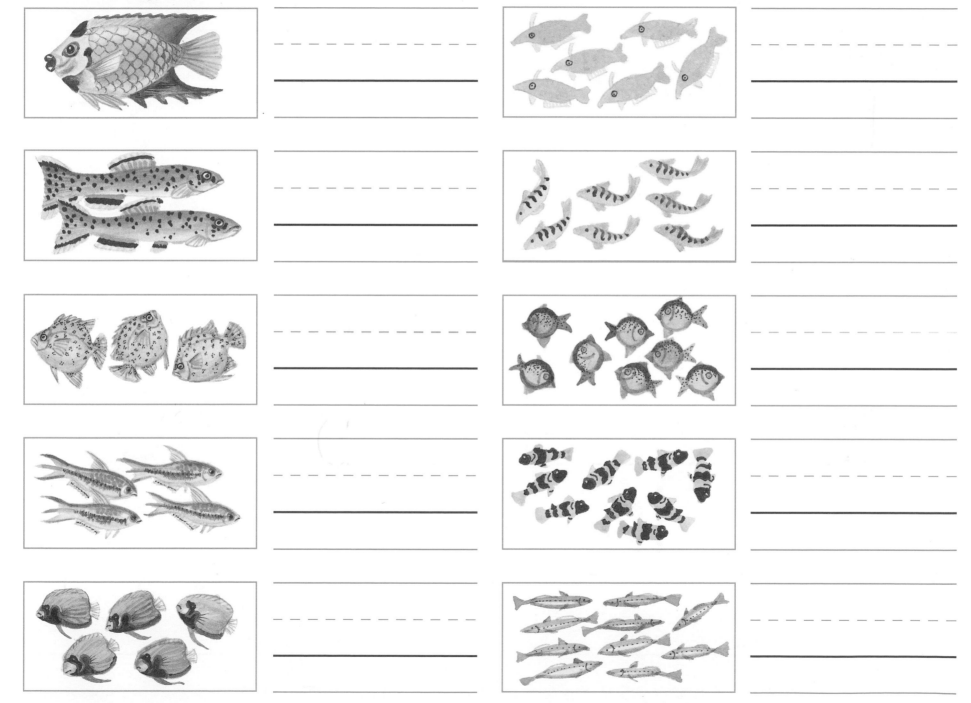

Write Number Words

Write the numerals and number words.

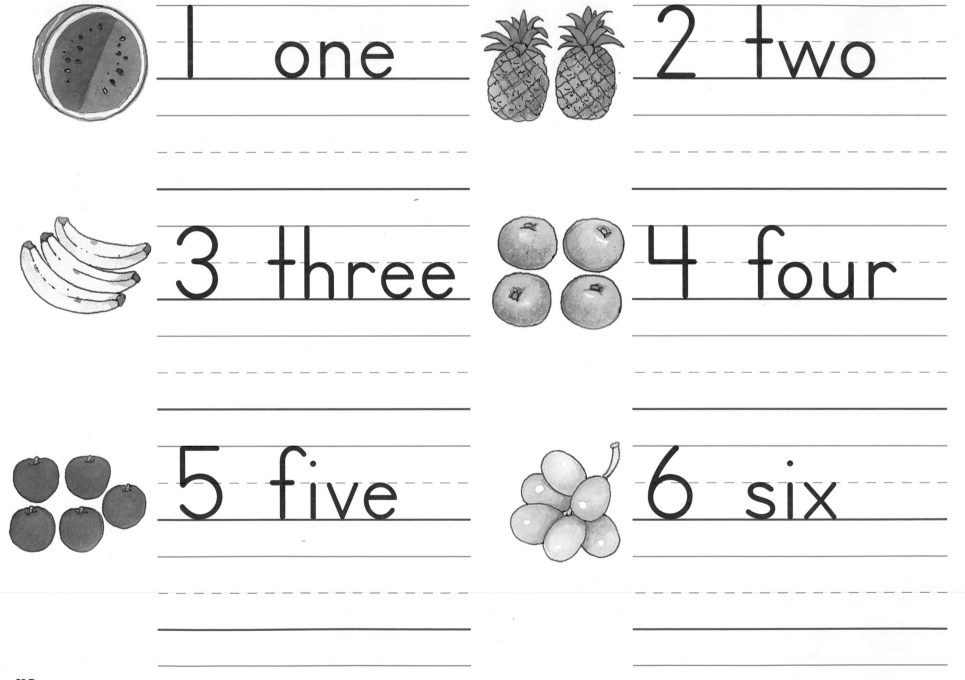

1 one

2 two

3 three

4 four

5 five

6 six

Write Words

Write the words.

dog   cat   sun   pig

dog   cat   sun   pig

Write Sentences

Write the sentences.

One dog plays piano.

Three dogs sing.

Write a Note

Write the note.

Dear Aunt Tess,

I miss you.　Get well.

Sammy

Write an Invitation

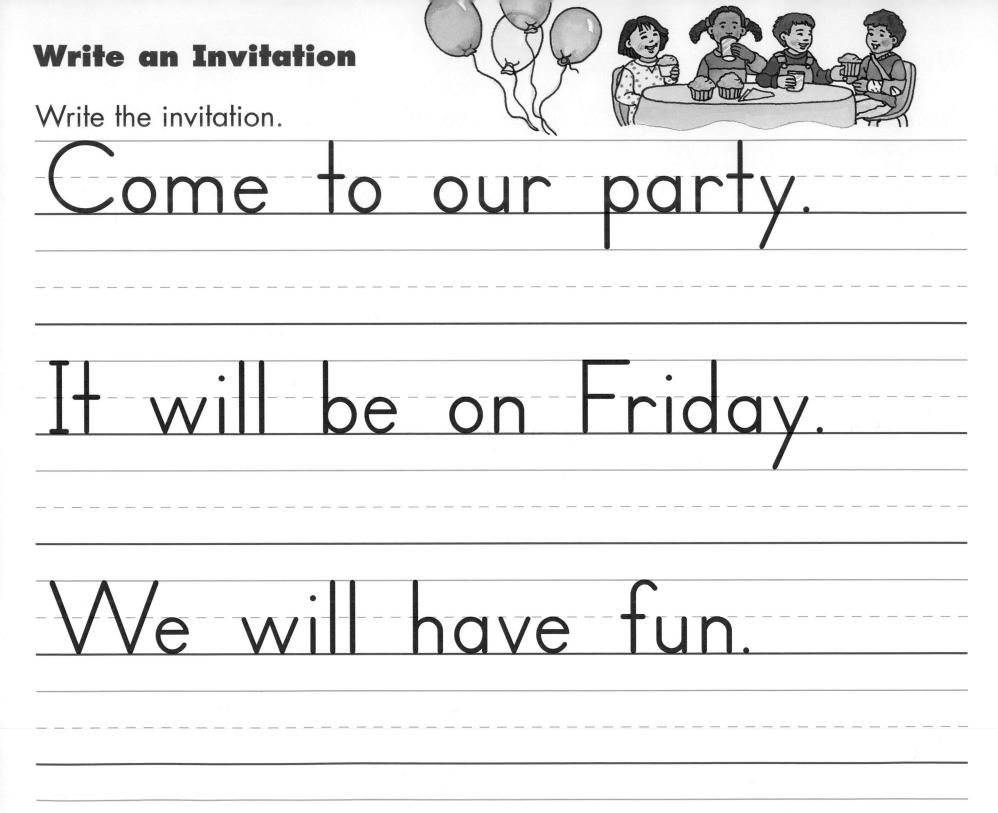

Write the invitation.

Come to our party.

It will be on Friday.

We will have fun.

Draw a picture.
Write words about your picture.

Index